Smoking kills

A White Paper on Tobacco

Presented to Parliament by the
Secretary of State for Health, and the Secretaries of State
for Scotland, Wales and Northern Ireland
by Command of Her Majesty

December 1998

Cm 4177

£11.50

Contents

Preface

In Britain today, more than 120,000 people are going to die over the next year from illnesses directly related to smoking. And the year after that, and the year after that. Unless we all do something.

I know these are statistics - sometimes hard to grasp and all too often too easy to dismiss. But they are powerful figures: each one is a testimony to individual and family suffering which need not happen. This appalling waste of people's lives, and the untold story behind it of misery and distress from cancer and heart disease, is wholly preventable. If people chose to stop smoking, they would live longer. Smoking kills.

Yet we recognise that people have a choice. We would like them to stop smoking, and to choose life. The detailed proposals set out in this White Paper, the first-ever in this country on smoking, will help them to make that choice. I reject completely that this is the so-called nanny state in action. It is instead the Government meeting what are clearly its responsibilities. Smokers have rights. So do non-smokers. Both have responsibilities - to themselves, to each other, to their families, and to the wider community. The Government too has responsibilities. Meeting them is what we were elected to do, and what we are determined to do. This White Paper on tobacco is a key part of keeping that promise. It is an important move which I believe will be a significant step towards achieving our goal of improving public health for all the people of Britain.

Tony Blair

The Rt Hon Tony Blair MP
Prime Minister

Foreword

Smoking kills. That has been known for years. That is why a lot of adults have given up smoking. But the number of adults who smoke has stopped falling. Worse still the number of children who smoke is going up, with more girls than boys taking up this deadly habit.

Smoking is now the principal avoidable cause of premature deaths in the UK. It hits the worst off people hardest of all. It harms people who do not smoke. It harms babies in the womb. That is why the Goverment is determined to turn things round. We want to help existing smokers quit the habit and help children and young people not to get addicted in the first place.

These objectives can only be achieved by a concerted campaign to reduce smoking. That is why this White Paper spells out a package of measures each of which will add to the impact of the others. A major part of the effort will be targeted on children.

As a result of this Government taking a positive position, a Europe wide ban on tobacco advertising and sponsorship is being introduced. This will be backed up by a powerful £50 million publicity campaign to shift attitudes and change behaviour. In collaboration with the Government, the hospitality industry will put in place measures to reduce the amount of smoking in public places. The Health and Safety Commission will be consulting on a new code of practice to protect people from other people's tobacco smoke at their place of work.

The White Paper also sets out our proposals to help the 7 out of every 10 smokers who say they want to quit. We are to invest up to £60 million to build the first ever comprehensive NHS service to help smokers to give up. This will be started first in those deprived communities which in England we have designated as Health Action Zones. The extra help, including nicotine replacement therapy, will be targeted at the worst off, who are most likely to smoke and least able to afford it.

This White Paper spells out a balanced package of measures which we are convinced will command public support and reduce the 120,000 deaths presently caused by smoking every year.

The Rt Hon Frank Dobson MP
Secretary of State for Health

The Rt Hon Donald Dewar MP
Secretary of State for Scotland

The Rt Hon Marjorie Mowlam MP
Secretary of State for Northern Ireland

The Rt Hon Alun Michael MP
Secretary of State for Wales

1 Smoking kills

'smoking kills more than 13 people an hour'

1.1 Smoking kills. Smoking is the single greatest cause of preventable illness and premature death in the UK. Smoking kills over 120,000 people in the UK a year - more than 13 people an hour[1]. Every hour, every day. For the EU as a whole the number of deaths from tobacco is estimated at well over 500,000 a year[2]. A generation after the health risks from smoking were demonstrated beyond dispute, smoking is still causing misery to millions. Smoking is still killing.

1.2 The Government is determined to see a major improvement in health in the UK. To help that, we have proposed tough and specific new targets for health improvement, backed with clear proposals for action to achieve them. Achieving these targets can only be done if we tackle smoking. One of the targets is to reduce cancer deaths. Another will be to reduce heart disease deaths. Cancer and heart disease are the two most common fatal diseases in this country. Smoking is a major cause of cancer and heart disease[1].

'achieving the targets and these key goals will give everyone in our country a better chance to enjoy a full, healthy and prosperous life. It cannot be done unless we tackle smoking'

1.3 The new targets will reinforce our key goals for public health improvement, which were set out with proposed targets in our consultative document earlier this year, *Our Healthier Nation*[3]. They are:

• to improve the health of the population as a whole by increasing the length of people's lives and the number of years people spend free from illness; and

• to improve the health of the worst off in society and to narrow the health gap

[1] The consultation document Our Healthier Nation was published for England in February 1998. Similar health strategies exist for Scotland - Working Together for a Healthier Scotland, Wales - Better Health Better Wales, and Northern Ireland - Regional Strategy for Health and Social Well-being 1997 to 2002.

Achieving the targets and these key goals will give everyone in our country a better chance to enjoy a full, healthy and prosperous life. It cannot be done unless we tackle smoking.

1.4 We made clear in our election manifesto that we intended to take action over smoking. We are doing so with the proposals we are publishing here. Tackling smoking is central to cutting deaths from cancer and heart disease. Tackling smoking is central to improving health in Britain.

Smoking - the facts

1.5 Tobacco first came to Britain in the sixteenth century. But smoking as a mass habit is a phenomenon of the twentieth century. So too is smoking as a mass killer.

1.6 Smoking peaked in the 1950s and 1960s, and fell steadily in the 1970s and 1980s[4]. Currently, there are around 13 million adult smokers in the UK[5]. But the long downward trend in smoking may be levelling out. Adult smoking rates rose in 1996, the last full year for which figures are available, for the first time since 1972. We may be seeing the beginning of a new upward trend in smoking. Among people aged 16 and over, the smoking rate of 28 per cent in England was the same as in 1992 and was up on the 1994 rate of 26 per cent[6]. The adult smoking rate is particularly high in Scotland and Wales at 32 per cent[6,7]. In Northern Ireland it is 29 per cent[8].

'smoking as a mass habit is a phenomenon of the twentieth century. So too is smoking as a mass killer'

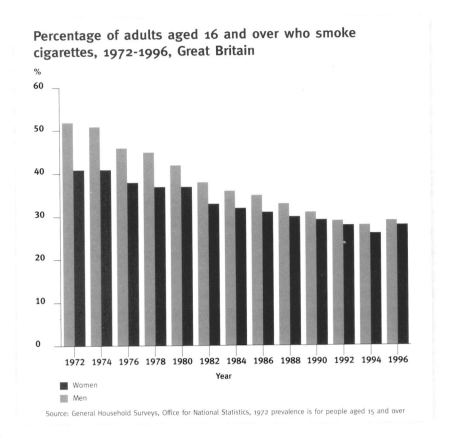

Percentage of adults aged 16 and over who smoke cigarettes, 1972-1996, Great Britain

Source: General Household Surveys, Office for National Statistics, 1972 prevalence is for people aged 15 and over

1.7 More and more children and young people are starting to smoke. The proportion of those aged 11 to 15 who smoke regularly was 8 per cent in England in 1988. In 1996 it was 13 per cent. The upward trend is particularly notable among girls. In 1988, just one in five 15-year-old girls smoked regularly. Now it is one in three[9].

'the vast majority of smokers take up the habit as teenagers - many will go on to smoke all their lives'

1.8 82 per cent of smokers take up the habit as teenagers[6]. Smoking is addictive, and many of the children and young people who smoke will go on to smoke all their lives.

1.9 Rising rates of children smoking are feeding through into rates of adult smoking as each successive generation gets beyond the age of 16.

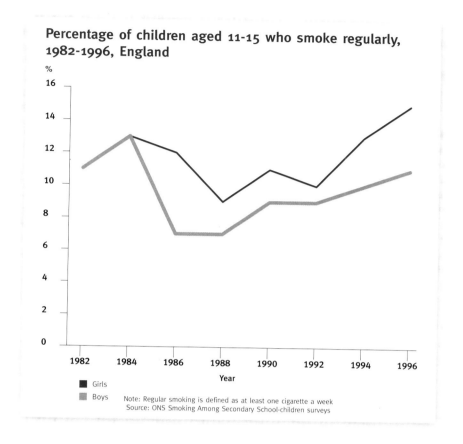

Percentage of children aged 11-15 who smoke regularly, 1982-1996, England

■ Girls

■ Boys   Note: Regular smoking is defined as at least one cigarette a week
Source: ONS Smoking Among Secondary School-children surveys

1.10 Internationally, Britain smokes heavily. While the availability and quality of smoking data varies considerably from country to country, according to World Health Organisation statistics on the quantity of cigarettes consumed per person, smokers in the UK consume about 25 per cent more than the EU average, though actual smoking rates in the UK are roughly at the average for the EU as a whole.

1.11 Other countries have had considerable success in reducing smoking rates. Norway, Finland and Iceland all introduced advertising bans back in the 1970s which were followed by hefty reductions in smoking rates or tobacco consumption[10]. Adult smoking rates in Finland were 22 per cent in 1996[11].

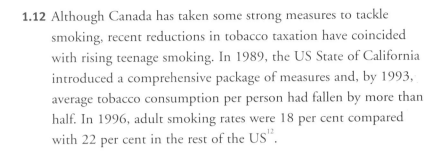

1.12 Although Canada has taken some strong measures to tackle smoking, recent reductions in tobacco taxation have coincided with rising teenage smoking. In 1989, the US State of California introduced a comprehensive package of measures and, by 1993, average tobacco consumption per person had fallen by more than half. In 1996, adult smoking rates were 18 per cent compared with 22 per cent in the rest of the US[12].

1.13 Smoking rates in the UK are considerably higher than those in places like California and Norway. The general experience of other countries is that comprehensive packages of measures can lead to significant reductions in smoking.

'for every 1000 20-year-old smokers it is estimated that one will be murdered, six will die in road accidents and 250 will die in middle age from smoking'

Smoking - the risks

1.14 Most people know that smoking is bad for health. Smoking, more than any other factor, cuts people's life expectancy. As well as being the prime cause of cancer and heart disease, it also causes many other fatal conditions and chronic illnesses among adults. The dangers of smoking are clear:

- over 120,000 people are killed a year because they smoke

- half of all who continue to smoke for most of their lives die of the habit; a quarter before the age of 69, and a quarter in old age[13], at time when average life expectancy is 75 for men and nearly 80 for women[14]

- those who smoke regularly and die of a smoking-related disease lose on average 16 years from their life expectancy compared to non-smokers[13]

- for every 1000 20-year-old smokers it is estimated that while one will be murdered and six will die in motor accidents, 250 will die in middle age from smoking, and 250 will die in older age from smoking[13]

- smoking is dangerous at any age, but the younger people start, the more likely they are to smoke for longer and to die early from smoking. Someone who starts smoking aged 15 is 3 times more likely to die of cancer due to smoking than someone who starts in their mid-20s[15]

- smoking causes 84% of deaths from lung cancer, and 83% of deaths from chronic obstructive lung disease, including bronchitis[1]

- smoking causes 46,500 deaths from cancer a year in the UK - 3 out of 10 cancer deaths[1]. As well as lung cancer, smoking can cause death by cancer of the mouth, larynx, oesophagus, bladder, kidney, stomach and pancreas[1]

- smoking causes 1 out of every 7 deaths from heart disease - 40,300 deaths a year in the UK from all circulatory diseases[1]

- smoking is also linked to many other serious conditions including asthma and brittle bone disease (osteoporosis)[16]

- levels of smoking are particularly high among people with severe mental illness[17]. This is likely to be one of the reasons why the severely mentally ill tend to die younger

- some ethnic groups in the UK favour chewed or other oral tobacco, notably betel quid. All forms of tobacco cause cancer[18]

- treating illness and disease caused by smoking is estimated to cost the NHS up to £1.7 billion every year in terms of GP visits, prescriptions, treatment and operations[19]

'treating illness and disease caused by smoking is estimated to cost the NHS up to £1.7 billion every year.

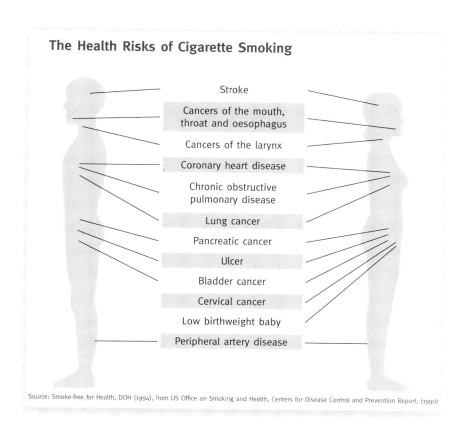

The Health Risks of Cigarette Smoking

Stroke

Cancers of the mouth, throat and oesophagus

Cancers of the larynx

Coronary heart disease

Chronic obstructive pulmonary disease

Lung cancer

Pancreatic cancer

Ulcer

Bladder cancer

Cervical cancer

Low birthweight baby

Peripheral artery disease

Source: Smoke-free for Health, DOH (1994), from US Office on Smoking and Health, Centers for Disease Control and Prevention Report, (1990)

1.15 The UK has high rates of death due to smoking compared to most other countries in the EU. Women under 65 in the UK have the worst death rate from lung cancer of all EU countries except Denmark. They also have the second worst death rate from heart disease after women in Ireland. Men under 65 in the UK have a lower than average death rate from lung cancer, but the third worst death rate from heart disease after men in Finland and Ireland[11].

Passive smoking

1.16 Passive smoking - breathing in other people's tobacco smoke- also kills. While most non-smokers are not exposed to levels of passive smoke sufficient for them to incur significant extra risk, many thousands are, such as those living with smokers or working in particularly smoky atmospheres for long periods of time. Non-smokers and smokers need to be made aware of the true risks.

'17,000 hospital admissions in a single year of children under 5 are due to their parents smoking'

1.17 Several hundred people a year in the UK are estimated to die from lung cancer brought about by passive smoking[20]. Passive smoking almost certainly also contributes to deaths from heart disease - an even bigger killer than lung cancer[21].

1.18 Passive smoking, even in low levels, can cause illness[18]. Asthma sufferers are more prone to attacks in smoky atmospheres. Children, more vulnerable than adults and often with little choice over their exposure to tobacco smoke, are at particular risk.

1.19 Children whose parents smoke are much more likely to develop lung illness and other conditions such as glue ear and asthma than children of non-smoking parents[22]. The Royal College of Physicians has estimated that as many as 17,000 hospital admissions in a single year of children under 5 are due to their parents smoking[23]. They also estimate that one quarter of cot deaths could be caused by mothers smoking. Women who smoke while pregnant are likely to reduce the birthweight, and damage the health, of their baby[24].

Smoking and inequalities

1.20 Smoking more than any other identifiable factor contributes to the gap in healthy life expectancy between those most in need, and those most advantaged[25]. While overall smoking rates have fallen over the decades, for the least advantaged they have barely fallen at all. In 1996, 12 per cent of men in professional jobs smoked, compared with 40 per cent of men in unskilled manual jobs.

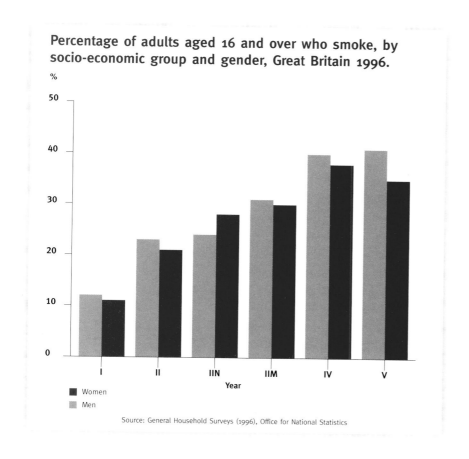

Percentage of adults aged 16 and over who smoke, by socio-economic group and gender, Great Britain 1996.

Source: General Household Surveys (1996), Office for National Statistics

1.21 Such differences are reflected in the impact of smoking on health. A higher rate of smoking among people in manual jobs is matched by much higher rates of disease such as cancer and heart disease.

1.22 Between 1991 and 1993, among men aged 20 to 64 in professional work, 17 in every 100,000 died of lung cancer, compared with 82 per 100,000 in unskilled manual work. For the same period and age group, among professional workers, 81 per 100,000 died from coronary heart disease compared with 235 per 100,000 in unskilled manual jobs[26].

'the cost of smoking is high in terms of people's health'

1.23 The close link between smoking and health inequalities was highlighted again recently in the report of the independent inquiry into health inequalities chaired by Sir Donald Acheson[27]. The report concluded that the relatively stable rate of smoking in the least advantaged groups suggests that simply intensifying current approaches would not be sufficient to tackle the problem.

Smoking - the cost

1.24 The cost of smoking is high in terms of people's health. But the cost of smoking is high in other ways too. Smoking is estimated to cost the NHS up to £1.7 billion every year[19]. And it costs families, especially the poorest, a great deal too. It is estimated that, in 1996, there were approximately 1 million lone parents on Income Support, of whom 55 per cent smoked an average of five packs of cigarettes a week at a cost of £2.50 per pack[28]. That means lone parent families spent a staggering £357 million on cigarettes during that year.

Smoking - Government action

'with their right to smoke, too, comes the responsibility to others who choose not to smoke'

1.25 The Government is determined to tackle these problems. The case for action on smoking is clear. Governments have tried in the past to reduce smoking. But while previous efforts have contributed to the steady reduction in the overall number of adults who smoke, success has been limited. Now, the rise in children smoking and the halt in the decline in adult smoking reinforces the case for new Government action. But at the same time, we recognise that Government action in areas of personal choice like smoking is a difficult and a sensitive issue. Tobacco is a uniquely dangerous product. If introduced today, it would not stand the remotest chance of being legal. But smoking is not against the law. We do not intend to make smoking unlawful. We are not banning smoking.

1.26 Currently, well over a quarter of the people of Britain smoke. The Government fully recognises their right to choose to do so. We will not in any of our proposals infringe upon that right. But with rights come responsibilities. Smokers have a responsibility to themselves - to their own health, and to ensure that in making the choice to smoke, their choice is based on a real understanding of the risks involved. With their right to smoke, too, comes the responsibility to others who choose not to smoke. Just as the Government is determined not to infringe upon people's rights to make free and informed choices, it is also determined to ensure that the responsibilities of smokers to people who choose not to smoke are carried out. That means a balance of rights and responsibilities - for those who smoke and for those who do not. Striking that balance is a clear and tough challenge - for the Government, for business, for local authorities, for voluntary groups and especially for individuals.

1.27 The Government has a clear role in tackling smoking. While it is for individuals to make their own choices about smoking, the impact of smoking on the people of Britain - on their health, in causing premature deaths, on non-smokers and in terms of its overall cost - is so great that if it were any other cause, the Government would face accusations of negligence for failing to take action. The Government also has a clear responsibility to protect children from tobacco.

1.28 Reducing smoking will save lives. The Government intends to implement a tough and comprehensive programme to ensure that those who smoke are aware of the potential consequences of their choice, that those who do not smoke are protected against those who do, and that the number of people smoking in Britain falls.

1.29 We have already taken action, especially in Europe. The Government's proposals in this White Paper set out the major steps we now intend to take. We will support this new programme of action, with new money - more than £100 million over the next three years. We recognise the scale of the challenge we all face to reduce smoking. But in partnership with others, we are determined to meet that challenge, and to improve the overall health of everyone - smokers and non-smokers alike - in our country.

'we will support this new programme of action, with new money - more than £100 million over the next three years'

2 Government action

2.1 The Government's strategy over smoking is clear. We want to see a reduction in smoking to improve health in Britain. To achieve that, we will implement a comprehensive and coherent package, with three clear objectives:

- to reduce smoking among children and young people

- to help adults - especially the most disadvantaged - to give up smoking

- to offer particular help to pregnant women who smoke

We will reinforce our measures with money - more than £100 million over three years†

We will draw on the experience of other countries which have successfully tackled smoking.

We will set targets for the tough action we are taking - targets which we will monitor closely.

'widespread public support... is essential for real, lasting change'

2.2 We believe the measures set out here are practical, reasonable, and will work. We believe they will have the widespread public support which is essential for real, lasting change.

What we have done

2.3 The Government has laid the foundations for the action set out in this White Paper. We have so far acted in a number of key areas:

- tobacco summit

- advertising

- tax

†£110 million in England, £8 million in Scotland and £1 million in Northern Ireland. Funding in Wales is subject to the outcome of the Comprehensive Spending Review for Wales.

Tobacco summit

What was the summit about?

2.4 We began to develop our proposals for this White Paper with an international summit on smoking in July 1997. Other countries had valuable experience and expertise which we wanted to learn from. Our aim was to take the best available advice on what we might do about smoking in the UK. Specialists from the UK and around the world gathered in London to work with us on identifying the key issues and the range of possible measures we could take. The specialists considered detailed options for the design and implementation of a ban on tobacco advertising, preventing children from smoking, helping people who want to quit, work and public places policies, consumer protection and tobacco taxation.

What did we learn?

2.5 The key message was that to make a lasting impact on smoking, we would need a wide and integrated range of measures. An end to tobacco advertising should be the cornerstone of any strategy, and be as broad as possible, including sponsorship and other forms of tobacco promotion. Any other measures we took would not work as well if they had to compete with stylish and powerful tobacco advertising. Without a range of further measures, ending tobacco advertising would not deliver a large enough impact on the problem.

Who else have we consulted?

2.6   The Government's approach over smoking needs the support of the public, and of major players like business. We believe it enjoys that support. But to ensure it does, we have discussed our approach widely. The summit began the process, and we continued with extensive discussions with health interests, tobacco manufacturers, and representatives of those who work in the tobacco industry. We have met with representatives of restaurateurs and publicans, with pressure groups and anti-smoking charities, with advertisers, and shopkeepers. A list of those we have consulted is provided at the end of this document.

2.7   The publication of this White Paper marks the end of the exploratory phase, and the start of a sustained period of change and progress. The White Paper builds on the changes in public attitudes to smoking over the last three decades.

'smoking is the greatest single cause of preventable illness and premature death in the UK. We will therefore ban tobacco advertising'

Advertising

Action in Europe

2.8   We gave a commitment in our election manifesto to take action on tobacco advertising:

Smoking is the greatest single cause of preventable illness and premature death in the UK. We will therefore ban tobacco advertising[29].

2.9   Since 1989, European Union member states had been discussing a law to end tobacco advertising and sponsorship. Some member states had already ended tobacco advertising, or were planning to. Others did not. The European Commission makes proposals for EU-wide measures to harmonise market rules among the member states where there are differences which cause market unevenness and hamper trade. In this case, the Commission proposed a Directive to harmonise the different rules, and, as required under European treaty arrangements, had regard to a high level of health protection in drawing up its proposals.

2.10 At the time, Britain was among the countries blocking the initiative. But following the election in May 1997, we joined with other member states to re-open negotiations on the Directive. We set three tests which would need to be met before we could support the Directive. We needed to be satisfied that the Directive:

- was properly based in EU law

- allowed enough time for business, sports and other organisations to adapt

- would end advertising but permit tobacco products to be displayed for normal sale

2.11 The Government entered into lengthy and detailed negotiations with our European partners. We negotiated for common sense and practicability. Only seven months after the election, the EU Council of Ministers was able to support the terms of the Directive. It was finally adopted on 22nd June 1998. Member states now have an obligation to put the Directive into their domestic legislation. Proposals to do so are set out in Chapter Five. They form the core of the steps we will be taking to tackle smoking in Britain.

Tax

Why action is needed

2.12 Research shows that the demand for tobacco products is related to their price[30]. As prices rise, demand falls. So high tax levels are one important means of reducing tobacco consumption. High tobacco prices are also a deterrent to children tempted to take up smoking. The real price of tobacco - that is, after allowing for inflation - has increased significantly in recent decades. But people's real incomes have also risen.

2.13 When people's incomes increase faster than the price of cigarettes, people can afford to buy more cigarettes - that is, the 'affordability' of cigarettes goes up. This can reduce the incentive to give up smoking presented by rising tobacco tax.

'when people's incomes increase faster than the price of cigarettes, the 'affordability' of cigarettes goes up'

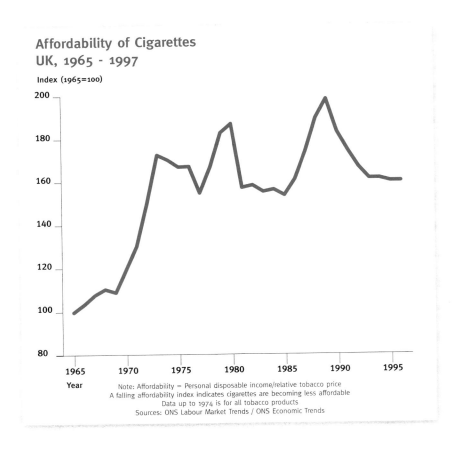

Affordability of Cigarettes
UK, 1965 - 1997

Index (1965=100)

Year

Note: Affordability = Personal disposable income/relative tobacco price
A falling affordability index indicates cigarettes are becoming less affordable
Data up to 1974 is for all tobacco products
Sources: ONS Labour Market Trends / ONS Economic Trends

'the price of a typical packet of 20 cigarettes at the end of 1998 is about 55p higher than at the end of 1996'

2.14 The graph above shows how the affordability of cigarettes has changed since 1965, when people first became aware of the great health risks associated with smoking[23]. Cigarettes are still over 60 per cent more affordable now than in 1965.

What action are we taking?

2.15 Tax - that is, duty and VAT - currently accounts for almost 80 per cent of the price of a packet of cigarettes. We set cigarette tax at a high level so that the price of cigarettes in the shops will be high. This acts as an incentive to smoke less.

2.16 The Government has committed itself to increases in tobacco taxation. As incomes tend to rise significantly each year, the only way to reduce affordability is to put tobacco tax up by more. The last Government said in 1993 that it would increase tobacco duty by at least 3 per cent in real terms each year. But we believe it is right to go further.

2.17 In our first Budget, in July 1997, the Chancellor announced that, in future, tobacco duties would be increased on average by at least 5 per cent in real terms a year. Tobacco duties rose by just over 5 per cent in real terms on both 1 December 1997 and again on 1 December 1998. The price of a typical packet of 20 cigarettes at the end of 1998 is about 55p higher than at the end of 1996.

2.18 Because of the high taxation of cigarettes, Governments are sometimes accused of exploiting smokers. The charge is made particularly in relation to smokers who are less well off, because tax and price increases hit most heavily those who spend the highest proportions of their income on tobacco.

2.19 We recognise this issue, which is why we are going to balance high tobacco tax with real support from the NHS to help smokers quit. No UK government has provided such support properly before. That is what we mean by a comprehensive approach to tackling smoking.

Summary

2.20 The Government believes it has taken a number of important steps over smoking. But the steps taken so far are only the start. Further action is now necessary if smoking is to be reduced, and health in Britain improved.

'we are going to balance high tobacco tax with real support from the NHS to help smokers quit'

3 Smoking and young people

Why do children start to smoke?

3.1 Children smoke for all sorts of reasons. Some smoke to show their independence, others because their friends do. Some smoke because adults tell them not to, others to follow the example of role models. There is no single cause. Parents, brothers and sisters who smoke are a powerful influence. So is advertising. So too is sport which is often sponsored by tobacco companies.

3.2 Many children experiment with smoking, believing they will be able to stop when they want to. But smoking is highly addictive and a great many will find themselves unable to give up.

'unless we take action, hundreds of children each day will continue to take up smoking'

3.3 Unless we take action, hundreds of children each day will continue to take up smoking. Smoking among the young is increasing year by year. Eighty two per cent of adult smokers start smoking in their teens. Some will manage to quit early, but many will continue to smoke for decades, unable to give up and increasingly at risk of serious illness and early death.

3.4 Most people know something about the health risks of smoking. But young smokers do not see the risks applying to them[31].

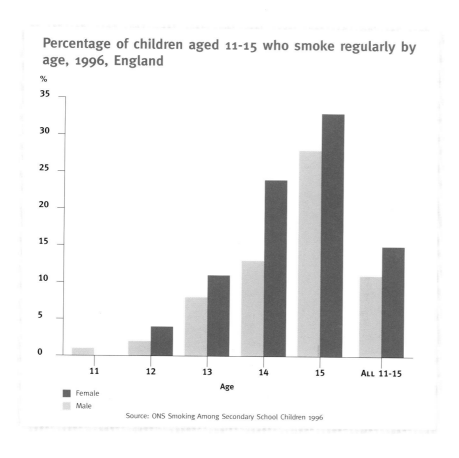

Percentage of children aged 11-15 who smoke regularly by age, 1996, England

Source: ONS Smoking Among Secondary School Children 1996

3.5 Among children aged 11, 1 per cent smoke at least once a week. But by the time they are 15 it is 30 per cent. The proportion of girls aged 15 who smoke at least one cigarette a week has increased from 22 per cent in 1988 to 33 per cent in 1996[9].

Percentage of 15 year olds who smoke regularly, 1982-1996, England

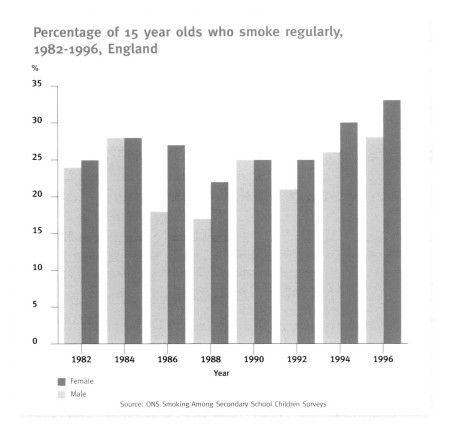

Source: ONS Smoking Among Secondary School Children Surveys

3.6 Some children will always experiment with smoking, whatever parents, teachers, doctors or Governments say. We need to make clear the risks of smoking to people of any age, and to counter the idea that there is any link between smoking and glamour, maturity and independence.

3.7 While we are unlikely to achieve success overnight, experience from other countries shows that success is possible if we adopt a comprehensive, sustained and properly resourced approach.

Action to protect children and young people

3.8   The Government believes that a range of steps will help protect young people both by making it less likely that they will begin to smoke and by helping them to stop:

- Minimal tobacco advertising in shops

- Tough enforcement on under age sales

- Proof of age card

- Strong rules on siting of cigarette vending machines

Minimal tobacco advertising in shops

Why action is needed

3.9   When children go into a shop to buy sweets or a magazine, they are now faced with cigarette adverts on the walls or hanging from the ceiling, tobacco-branded till covers, dispensers with cigarette special-offer leaflets or any other tobacco promotion material.

3.10   The Government believes that this is harmful to children, and increases the likelihood of their starting to smoke. The EU Directive dose not apply to 'advertising aimed at purchasers' at the locations at which tobacco is actually sold. It is up to the UK to define what that means when we regulate to implement the Directive in this country.

3.11   We want children to be able to go into shops without being faced with tobacco adverts or promotional materials. We have had detailed discussions with the retail sector to hear their views. Shopkeepers would like to retain the wall fixture (or 'gantry') for displaying tobacco products. Gantries are usually on the wall behind or near the till. Shopkeepers also want to continue to be able to put a poster in their window, or elsewhere, giving details of the prices of various tobacco products to customers who already smoke.

'we want children to be able to go into shops without being faced with tobacco adverts or promotional materials'

No tobacco advertising in its stores - the Co-op

Co-op stores sell tobacco, but the Co-op already operates a policy of not promoting tobacco within its stores in any way which could glamourise or induce people to smoke. This means:

- no cigarettes sales stands featuring manufacturers' advertising
- no branded promotional material such as clocks, signs
- no tobacco products or advertising in shop windows
- shelf edges only feature price information
- no tobacco priced lower than its main competitors

a) Shops in general

3.12 Subject to our obligation to implement the Directive faithfully, we intend to define what is meant by "advertising aimed at purchasers" in such a way as to limit it strictly to the gantries displaying tobacco products themselves and their prices. In doing so, we will be aiming to protect children as far as possible from exposure to pro-tobacco messages in shops, whilst taking account of the legitimate desire of retailers to display products for sale and indicate their prices.

b) Specialist tobacconists

3.13 The Directive also provides a specific exemption for advertising in shops specialising in tobacco products. Britain has some 350 specialist tobacconists. They sell mainly cigars and pipe tobacco which do not appeal to children and young people. We therefore do not believe it need be necessary to restrict advertising, by regulation, in specialist tobacconists. Nevertheless, we need to ensure that children are adequately protected from exposure to tobacco advertising.

3.14 We have therefore agreed with Associated Independent Tobacco Specialists, the trade association, that no cigarettes, nor any advertising appealing to children or young people, will appear in specialist tobacconists' shop windows. Advertising inside specialist shops will continue as present.

3.15 Our regulations to implement the EC Directive will include a definition of specialist tobacconists to prevent the concession to specialist tobacconists being exploited to create new 'specialist' cigarette outlets designed to appeal to children or young people. We envisage that the definition will be in terms of the relative size of their non-cigarette tobacco business, to reflect the present nature of genuine specialist businesses.

Tough enforcement on under age sales

Why action is needed

3.16 Although it is illegal to sell cigarettes to anyone under 16, it is clear that the existing law is not being applied effectively.

3.17 Most children who smoke say they buy their cigarettes from shops[9]. Of those children who get their cigarettes from shops, only 22 per cent of boys and 15 per cent of girls in England say they found it difficult[9]. That suggests that many shopkeepers are selling tobacco to children.

3.18 The majority of shopkeepers say they question children they suspect of being under 16 when they try to buy tobacco. But many 14 and 15-year olds can and do pass for 16. We recognise the problems busy shopkeepers face in refusing to sell tobacco to such customers.

3.19 We believe that the majority of shopkeepers do try hard to avoid illegal sales. But we are going to work with local enforcement agencies to make sure shopkeepers comply with the law much more successfully.

'although it is illegal to sell cigarettes to anyone under 16, it is clear that the existing law is not being applied effectively'

'we want to build on what is being done successfully in some authorities to bring all authorities up to the standard of the best'

3.20 The first priority should be to help shopkeepers comply with the existing regulations. Legal action can be taken against those who flout their legal responsibilities. Under the Children and Young Persons (Protection from Tobacco) Act 1991[†], local authorities have a statutory duty to consider taking enforcement action at least once a year[‡]. However, not all local authorities do carry out checks in a typical year despite the clear problem. The legal powers are there, but they are not being rigorously applied.

The action we are taking

3.21 We are developing a new *Enforcement Protocol*, with representatives of local authorities, trading standards officers and environmental health officers, for use by local authorities in carrying out their duty under the 1991 Act. Every local authority should be properly exercising its statutory role in preventing under-age sales in accordance with best practice. We want to learn from what is being done successfully in some authorities to bring all authorities up to the standard of the best. This will build on the Best Value approach.

3.22 The Local Government Association (LGA) and the Local Authorities Co-ordinating body on Food and Trading Standards (LACOTS) are committed to work with the Government to ensure we make the best possible use of existing legislation. We will also be closely involving bodies representing local authorities and enforcement agencies in Scotland, Wales and Northern Ireland.

3.23 There is currently no statutory obligation on local authorities to carry out an enforcement campaign. But the LGA and LACOTS agree with us that every local authority should assess the need for such a campaign and, where a campaign is decided on, it should be run in accordance with recognised best practice. Together we will draw up a detailed protocol of best practice for use by local authorities UK-wide. The scope of the protocol is set out below:

[†] In Northern Ireland, the Children and Young Persons (Protection from Tobacco) (Northern Ireland) Order 1991.

[‡] Home Office Circular 17/1992 gave guidance about this.

Enforcement protocol for local authorities

- publishing a clear statement on dealing with under-age tobacco sales (and other age-restricted products)

- assessing the current local degree of compliance, the action required by trading standards officers to enforce it, high risk areas or particular outlets for targeted attention

- considering the parties with which consultation should take place before the annual review of enforcement action required under section 5(1)(a) of the Children and Young Persons (Protection From Tobacco) Act 1991

- acting in accordance with the joint central/local government Enforcement Concordat, with its emphasis on education and help to ensure compliance, with enforcement action concentrated on those who most flagrantly fail to comply with their obligations

- stressing the importance of local support for moves to introduce a proof of age card scheme as the key tool to enable retailers to meet their obligations with confidence

- using test purchasing, where permissible, either with under-age children or those who clearly look under-age to gather information about premises likely to be breaching the law or to assist prosecutions

- detailing enforcement action taken, prosecutions and fines, to act as a deterrent

- monitoring the action taken and the evaluation of its impact on the scale of the local problem, to inform the next year's statutory review

3.24 A constructive approach by trading standards officers helping retailers meet their responsibilities, combined with enforcement activity targeted at likely problem retailers, should lead to a significant improvement overall.

3.25 If local authorities carry out their obligations under the law in accordance with the kind of guidance outlined above, we can expect much better compliance with the law.

3.26 However, we will expect trading standards officers (enviromental health officers in Northern Ireland) to continue to press for the prosecution of persistent offenders. There will always be cases where prosecution is the only response for shopkeepers who deliberately flout the law.

3.27 Very effective action is already being taken by several local authorities.

'we will expect trading standards officers to continue to press for the prosecution of persistent offenders'

North Yorkshire Trading Standards

North Yorkshire County Council Trading Standards were pioneers in using young people in test purchases of cigarettes as a means of law enforcement. Test purchases give Trading Standards Officers an indication of the illegal tobacco sales problem in their area, and provide them with evidence they can use to prosecute retailers who break the law. North Yorkshire County Council have found that regular test purchasing and a high profile media approach have been extremely successful in reducing the incidents of reported sales of cigarettes to people under 16. The Public Protection Committee have illustrated their commitment by issuing the following statement:

"North Yorkshire County Council Trading Standards Department will:

- bring prosecutions in respect of offences under the Children & Young Persons Act 1933 (as amended) in respect of the sale of tobacco to children

- investigate fully complaints in respect of alleged offences under those provisions

- take other measures intended to reduce the incidence of offences under those provisions including:

  a) spot checks on retailers,

  b) maximising the use of media by the publication of warnings, successful prosecutions and health information where appropriate.

- act on any information concerning the location of cigarette vending machines on premises where children have access.

North Yorkshire Public Protection Committee will:

Consider at least once each year the enforcement programme in relation to this legislation and the extent to which any such programme has been carried out during the previous 12 months."

3.28 For such offenders, there is scope for making more use of the full range of penalties within the current limit on fines. The maximum fine for this offence was raised in 1991 to £2,500. The average fine is around a tenth of that figure.

3.29 Prosecutions for selling tobacco to under-16s are relatively rare, and magistrates and trading standards officers may need to consider in greater detail the issues surrounding such offences and the ways in which such cases can best be presented to courts. The Magistrates' Association and LACOTS will be discussing how these cases should be approached following this White Paper. As Parliament has provided a maximum fine of £2,500, there needs to be a clear understanding of the circumstances which could justify the higher levels of fine, such as previous convictions, or sales to particularly young children clearly well below the legal age.

3.30 Occasionally there will be individuals who flout the law and do so repeatedly. We do not believe that people who are prepared to behave so irresponsibly should be allowed to continue to sell tobacco. The Government will explore the scope for new measures to stop repeat offenders or their staff from selling tobacco. In principle, we favour the introduction of a new criminal sanction to deal with this problem, and will be looking carefully at the practicality of introducing and enforcing such a measure.

Prevention of illegal sales of tobacco in Belfast

Belfast City Council are seeking to prevent sales of cigarettes to children by developing both education and inspection policies. Retail outlets are visited twice yearly, and particular attention is paid to shops near schools. Children are used as 'test' buyers of cigarettes so that the enforcers can assess the scale of the problem and prosecute shopkeepers who may be flouting the law. Retailers are informed of their duties and how best to comply with the law through advisory leaflets and education programmes. Advice for retailers who employ part-time or temporary staff, or who have a high staff turnover is a high priority.

Essex Trading Standards proof of age card

Essex trading standards officers have developed a multi-purpose proof of age card. The card was devised with the help and co-operation of local organisations such as the County Education Department, Police, Health Promotion Officers and Head Teachers and, most importantly, the Council's Elected Members have taken a close interest in the project and supported it fully.

At least 3000 cards have already been issued and over half the schoolchildren in Essex will be issued with cards by early 1999. The cards are popular not only with young people, but also shopkeepers and law enforcement officers who know that any young person should be able to prove their age. In a recent exercise, young people trying to buy cigarettes were used to 'test' the response of shopkeepers, 75% were asked for the card.

Where these cards have been introduced, the number of complaints about illegal sales of age-restricted goods has already decreased, it is easier to target resources, and magistrates are taking a stronger line in cases of under-age sales.

Essex Trading Standards are sharing their experience with a number of interested authorities throughout England.

Proof-of-age card

Why action is needed

3.31 Local enforcement policies are particularly effective when backed by a simple and readily acceptable way for young people to prove their age, as the Essex example shows. This, more than anything else, is the plea we have heard from retailers.

3.32 A cross-industry proof of age card could enable retailers to avoid illegal sales of a whole range of age-restricted products including alcohol, fireworks, videos, lottery tickets and tobacco. A single card, available anywhere in the country, would enable all retailers to ask for the same proof of age. It would remove the doubts and arguments and could be supported by retailing associations and major chains. A standard policy of 'No proof - no sale' would give retailers confidence in complying with the law.

3.33 A number of proof of age schemes already exist, covering different products or different geographical areas. Some people believe that setting up a 'proof of age' scheme should be a job for the Government. But the industries which produce and sell age restricted products to the public have an obvious responsibility themselves to help retailers ensure that their products do not get into the wrong hands.

3.34 One such scheme has been established by the Portman Group, an independent company funded by the drinks industry to promote sensible drinking and to combat alcohol misuse. To help avoid sales of alcoholic drinks to under-18s, it established in 1990 the Portman Card: a photographic proof of age scheme available through retailers. The Card is free to applicants; there is a charge to retailers to help cover processing of applications. The card is estimated to reach about 1 in 7 new 18 year-olds. However, given the range of age-restricted products now available (and the different ages at which purchase is lawful), it clearly makes sense to build on the experience of the Portman Card and consider the feasibility of a multi-purpose proof of age card.

3.35 Initiatives such as the "Validate" scheme in Wales which was devised in response to local needs, could well provide further useful evidence as a workable national scheme is developed.

VALIDATE   **Validate proof of age scheme, Wales**

The VALIDATE proof of age card scheme was devised by Neath Port Talbot Trading Standards Department to ensure age-restricted products are not sold to people who are under age, and also to allow people who may appear younger to buy these products if they are of age. The scheme's success has depended on the collaboration and commitment of the local business community, trading standards and schools. The scheme was piloted in Dwr y Felin Comprehensive School in Neath. The success of this pilot has encouraged other local authorities to adopt the scheme, so that it now covers virtually all of South Wales.

What action are we taking

3.36 We have invited leading industrial figures to discuss the problem with us and to consider how best they could address it.

3.37 We believe that the producers of age-restricted goods should now work together to produce a single system, to enable retailers to meet their legal obligations with confidence by only selling restricted products to young people who can prove their age.

Strong rules on siting of cigarette vending machines to prevent their use by children

Why action is needed

3.38 The Office of National Statistics survey shows that one in three school children in England who smoke say that machines are one of their usual sources of cigarettes[9]. While other survey figures suggest lower levels, cigarette machines are clearly a significant source of cigarettes for school children.

3.39 This issue requires specific action. In crowded spaces, such as pubs, it is not always easy for busy members of staff to spot children using machines.

What action is being taken?

3.40 NACMO, the National Association of Cigarette Machine Operators, issues a code to its members defining the siting arrangements which they should follow. Following discussions with the Department of Health, NACMO has revised its rules so that the primary consideration when siting a machine is now the need to prevent sales to children.

3.41 The new code provides clear guidance to machine operators on the siting arrangements expected. A machine should be sited in a monitored, supervised area so that staff can be sure of preventing its use by young people. The code makes clear the need for siting requirements to be explained by the operator to a member of staff who will be responsible for supervising and maintaining control over the machine. It sets out essential conditions to be fulfilled by all operators to minimise the likelihood of their use by children. There is now no excuse for machine operators or pub, club and restaurant managers to site machines inappropriately.

3.42 NACMO are committed to making their own efforts to ensure the new rules are followed in practice. It should not be possible to find any cigarette vending machine to which children could have access unnoticed by a responsible member of staff. Details of any vending machines failing to comply should be sent to NACMO at NACMO, Resources for Business, PO Box 132, Macclesfield, Cheshire SK11 6FL.

'cigarette machines are clearly a significant source of cigarettes for school children'

4 Smoking and adults

4.1 Seven out of ten adult smokers say they would like to give up if they could[32]. But most smokers find it hard to quit. Even those who do manage to give up may have tried many times before they finally succeed. The urge to smoke can last for years, and many ex-smokers find it very easy to start smoking again. But for smokers who do give up, the chances of getting a serious or fatal disease are greatly reduced[33]. We want to help them in the most effective way we can.

4.2 Research has been done on how best to help people give up smoking. Research shows that there is a range of cheap and effective ways of helping people to quit. Doctors and other health professionals such as nurses, dentists and pharmacists can advise smokers to give up in the course of their day-to-day contact with them for health services. Not surprisingly, when a doctor talks to a smoker about the benefits of giving up, it can be a powerful motivator[34].

'nicotine replacement therapy doubles the chances of quitting successfully'

4.3 At the other end of the scale, a full course of specialist counselling combined with nicotine replacement therapy can lead up to 25 per cent of smokers to give up[35]. Although such methods may not work for everyone, they can significantly increase the chances of giving up successfully. The research also shows that, whatever kind of support is given by doctors and experts, nicotine replacement therapy doubles the chances of quitting successfully[34].

4.4   We know that many smokers do not want to quit, and that is their choice. But they should make that choice in the full knowledge of the risks and with the offer of support to help with their addiction if they want it.

4.5   They should also make their choice in the full knowledge of what are the benefits of quitting. Giving up smoking has immediate and longer-term effects. When a typical smoker quits, after:

20 minutes Blood pressure and pulse rate return to normal. Circulation improves in hands and feet, making them warmer.

8 hours Oxygen levels in the blood return to normal. Chances of a heart attack start to fall.

24 hours Carbon monoxide is eliminated from the body. The lungs start to clear out mucus and other debris.

48 hours Nicotine is no longer detectable in the body. The ability to taste and smell is improved.

72 hours Breathing becomes easier as the bronchial tubes relax. Energy levels increase.

2-12 weeks Circulation improves throughout the body, making walking easier.

3-9 months Breathing problems such as coughing, shortness of breath, and wheezing improve. Overall, lung function is increased by 5-10%.

5 years Risk of a heart attack falls to about half that of a smoker.

10 years Risk of lung cancer falls to about half that of a smoker. Risk of a heart attack falls to about the same as someone who has never smoked.
Source: QUIT®[36]

QUIT
Helping smokers to quit

4.6   Taking positive steps to help people give up smoking is not only important in improving the health of the individuals concerned. There will also be wider economic benefits. For example, there will be fewer days off work with illnesses caused by smoking and less pressure on hospital beds.

NHS smoking cessation services

What we are going to do

4.7 For the first time ever in the history of the NHS, we are investing substantial resources - up to £60 million of new money in England alone over the next three years - to build NHS services to help smokers who want to give up. High priority will be given to the development of services in each of the four UK countries[†]. The new service will mean that GPs and others will be able to refer smokers who really want to give up for a course of specialist counselling, advice and support. Smokers motivated to give up will also be able to enrol for courses where available without being referred. Each local service will be able to tailor the support it offers to suit the needs of smokers locally.

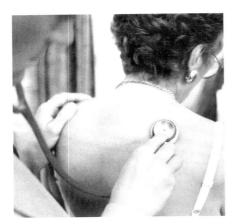

4.8 As part of the package, counsellors will offer a week's supply of nicotine replacement therapy (NRT) - free of charge to those smokers least able to afford it - to introduce smokers to the potential benefit of NRT in relieving withdrawal symptoms.

4.9 The new services will be located, at first, in areas of greatest need. In 1999/00, year one, the Health Action Zones in England will receive £10 million, ring-fenced specifically for these services. Funding will be increased to £20 million in year two and £30 million in year three, to develop services more widely, subject to evidence of the effectiveness of the investment.

4.10 These are our intentions. We will continue to develop the practical detail of our plans so that services can be up and running as soon after 1 April 1999 as possible.

[†]Priority will be given for NHS smoking cessation services across the UK. As well as in England, resources have been identified for services in Scotland (£3m). In Northern Ireland, services will be provided within the overall funding for health. In Wales, funding is subject to the outcome of the Comprehensive Spending Review in Wales.

The role of all health professionals

4.11 Most people see their GP at least once a year[6], and other health professionals at other times during the year. But at the same time, less than half of smokers say they remember being given advice on smoking by a GP, practice nurse or other medical person at any point during the last five years[32].

4.12 GPs, practice nurses, midwives, dentists, pharmacists, health visitors and other health professionals are the people to whom we all look to advise us about our health. Each of those professions has an important role to play in giving the kind of smoking cessation advice which a modern health service ought to provide. Such advice need not take long; the consistency of the message is all important. Smokers need to be aware that those who know about health, advise against smoking. All health professionals working in hospital or community settings should assess smoking habits and provide advice to smokers on giving up, whenever possible.

4.13 Now that we will be investing substantial resources in specialist services, health professionals will have something more to offer patients who smoke. But expert advice will still be needed from health professionals in the course of everyday appointments, check-ups and treatment. Smoking is the biggest single threat to health faced by large sections of the population. It is important that all health professionals provide simple advice to give up smoking on as routine a basis as possible.

NRT on the NHS

4.14 To quit successfully, smokers also need to be strongly motivated and able to deal with the inevitable cravings for nicotine. That is where NRT comes in. A course of NRT provides the body with nicotine in decreasing doses until the craving is small enough to cope with. It also provides nicotine without any harmful smoke. NRT is not a miracle cure for nicotine addiction, but it can work for many smokers when used in accordance with the instructions and in the recommended quantities.

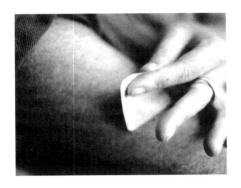

4.15 Many smokers are unaware of the potential benefits of NRT. It is usually cheaper than cigarettes (about £10 to £20 a week, compared with about £25 a week to support a 20-a-day habit) and only works if people do not smoke at the same time. It is available over the counter in pharmacies. We are going to raise the profile of NRT and encourage smokers to try it, particularly those who are least able to afford to smoke or buy NRT. Research shows that NRT is most effective in the context of skilled advice and support[34].

4.16 To those less well-off smokers who are prepared also to receive the specialist advice and support with which it works best, we will be providing one-week's free NRT. This fits with the evidence which shows that smokers who manage to avoid smoking for a complete week with the help of NRT are more likely to go on to quit for good[37]. A course of NRT typically lasts only about ten weeks. After that, someone who was spending £25 a week on cigarettes would be able to spend that money on something else.

4.17 We will monitor the effectiveness of this policy over the coming three years to see if alternative approaches to NRT would be better.

NRT in shops

4.18 At present, the law allows NRT to be sold only in pharmacies. However, the Committee on Safety of Medicines (CSM) has advised that low dose nicotine gum could be put on general sale in shops to help with smoking cessation[†].The CSM has also advised that a legal mechanism should be sought to prevent sales of NRT to those under 16. The Medicines Control Agency (MCA) is currently consulting on this issue and any views should be sent by 24 December 1998 to Room 1109A Market Towers, 1 Nine Elms Lane, London SW8 5NQ. We will consider any advice from the MCA following the consultation.

[†] Consultation letter MLX 248 has been issued to over 140 interested organisations to seek their views on the proposal.

Co-operating to improve cessation

4.19 We are going to work closely with the manufacturers of NRT products, with high street retail chemists, and with the medical professions to improve the provision of on-the-spot advice and NRT in as wide a range of settings as possible. We all recognise our common aim in increasing the number of people giving up smoking. A group of organisations has made the following statement of their intent.

Statement of intent

We welcome the Government's drive against smoking as a leading cause of preventable illness. Pharmacists in both community and hospital practice are particularly well placed to provide counselling, advice and support to smokers on how to give up, and on the range of medical products available to help them do so. We see community pharmacies, and pharmacies in hospital practice, as an integral part of good local smoking cessation services, and we are keen to co-operate with the NHS, and others at a local level, to develop and evaluate them. We believe there is also scope for further development of the role of community pharmacies as health promotion settings, and the support of pharmacists in public health is important here. We look forward to a developing partnership with the Government on smoking cessation.

Guild of Healthcare Pharmacists

THE NATIONAL PHARMACEUTICAL ASSOCIATION

National Pharmacists Association

Company Chemists' Association

Royal Pharmaceutical Society of Great Britain

Action for the least advantaged smokers

4.20 Our priority will be the need to help the least well off smokers. Smoking is disproportionately high among the more disadvantaged. If we are to reduce smoking overall, and reduce health inequalities, we must start with the groups who smoke the most.

4.21 Couples on Income Support who smoke, spend 15% of their entire incomes on tobacco[38]. That leaves less money to buy healthy food and other necessities for good health. The Exchequer receives much of the money spent on tobacco in the form of duty. But we would much rather people gave up smoking altogether.

4.22 The new NHS money will immediately go to areas of greatest deprivation. In England it will go from April 1999 to areas designated as Health Action Zones (HAZs). The 26 HAZs cover many of the most deprived areas in England. We have set up HAZs to drive up the standards of health among the poorest at a faster rate than for the general population. Smoking, with its clear link to health inequalities, is a critical issue in every HAZ.

'healthy living centres could also be used as a focal point for the local service.'

Scotland

Women, Low Income and Smoking Project, Scotland

Run by the Wester Hailes Health Agency and operating in one of the poorer districts of Edinburgh, this project centres on helping women on low income, young single mothers and OAPs to quit smoking.

The project is one of a wide range of community based initiatives running as part of the "Women, Low Income and Smoking Project" under the overall management of ASH (Scotland) and funded by the Health Education Board for Scotland. The programme uses a variety of approaches ranging from health and fitness sessions to magazine production and encourages the development of peer education.

4.23 From year two, we will begin to distribute the funds more widely across the whole country. Smokers of all kinds will be able to make use of the service, but the priority will continue to be helping the most disadvantaged smokers who want to quit. The free week's NRT will be provided against criteria that ensure it goes to the least advantaged.

4.24 Our new campaign to change attitudes to smoking (see Chapter Six) will also be designed and targeted to reach out to areas of high smoking and social deprivation. National smoking cessation helplines like the Quitline® will continue to be an important part of the service.

What the NHS should do now

4.25 The importance of advising and supporting smokers with attempts to give up is clearly flagged in the priorities guidance issued to the NHS, such as, in England, the National Priorities Guidance and the forthcoming National Service Framework for coronary heart disease.

4.26 We expect health authorities and health boards across the country to plan services in the light of the priorities guidance and in partnership with local authorities and other agencies. Health improvement programmes should include comprehensive local strategies to tackle smoking. The local health service should also set its own local targets to focus effort and monitor progress. We will issue more detailed guidance in early 1999 about what should be done with the new money. In the meantime, health authorities and boards should be taking steps to assess local needs so that from 1 April 1999 we can begin to make immediate progress.

4.27 The specialist services should be set up wherever smokers locally would most benefit. For example, they could be run in shopping centres, community centres, hospitals, or town halls. Healthy living centres could be used as a focal point for the local service. Counsellors could come from a range of health professional backgrounds.

4.28 A number of tools are available to NHS planners and health professionals to help them in setting up and delivering local smoking cessation services. We have commissioned the Health Education Authority (HEA) to develop smoking cessation guidelines for health professionals, which they have done with the endorsement of professional bodies[34]. In conjunction with the University of York, the HEA has also developed a resource which sets out the issues and costs involved in developing specialist cessation services[48].

Maudsley Clinic

The Addiction Resource Centre at the Bethlehem and Maudsley NHS Trust runs a specialist smoking cessation clinic. Smokers can refer themselves or be referred by a doctor. This clinic achieves a success rate of 20-25% a year, compared to 1% of smokers giving up on their own. Smokers are helped by trained staff either in group therapy or one-to-one sessions. They are also given nicotine replacement therapy at a reduced cost. The team at the Maudsley not only help people to give up smoking but also train professionals, like GPs and practice nurses, to help people quit.

5 Smoking and pregnant women

Smoking during pregnancy

5.1 Smoking during pregnancy harms the unborn child and leads to lower birthweight. New evidence also shows that women who smoke during pregnancy pass harmful carcinogens on to their baby[39].

5.2 24 per cent of women smoke during pregnancy, and only 33 per cent of women smokers give up during pregnancy[40]. The main reason is that smoking is addictive and is very hard to give up. We need to make people more aware of the serious risks of smoking during pregnancy and to offer them help when they try to give up.

5.3 Many parents continue to smoke at home while bringing up children. Children of smoking parents are more likely to suffer illness or even cot death. They are also much more likely to take up smoking themselves[9]. Almost half of single women smoke during pregnancy[40].

'children of smoking parents are more likely to suffer illness or even cot death'

5.4 The problems of smoking during pregnancy are closely related to health inequalities between those in need and the most advantaged. Women with partners in manual groups are more likely to smoke during pregnancy than those with partners in non-manual groups: 26 per cent of women with partners in manual groups smoke during pregnancy, compared with 12 per cent with partners doing non-manual work[40].

5.5 Helping pregnant women to give up smoking not only leads to health gains for mothers and their children, it can also mean immediate cost savings for the NHS. This is because smoking in pregnancy leads to low birthweight babies who may need very costly intensive care treatment. Savings to the NHS can amount to between three and six times the cost of providing help to pregnant women to give up smoking[19].

5.6 There is good evidence that helping pregnant women to give up smoking is cost-effective. Of course, many health professionals, particularly midwives and primary care teams, already provide advice to stop smoking to women smokers when they become pregnant.

What we are going to do

5.7 Pregnant women who smoke will be a key focus of action at local level as our new NHS smoking cessation services are developed. In Health Action Zones, where many of those women most in need live, up to £60 million in new money will flow from April 1999, to deliver expert help where it is most needed.

Clwyd Smoking in Pregnancy

The Clywd Smoking in Pregnancy project is targeted at all pregnant women in North East Wales. Its aim is to increase the quit rate in pregnant women and to help ensure they do not start smoking again in the months after their baby is born. The project includes training for professionals, such as doctors, midwives and nurses; structured help for women; and evaluation to see how well the project has worked. The ultimate aim is to ensure help in quitting is available to all pregnant smokers, as part of their pre-natal care.

5.8 At the moment, nicotine replacement therapy (NRT) is not advocated in the UK for pregnant women. However, the American Agency for Health Care Policy and Research has suggested that NRT should be offered in pregnancy to the heaviest smokers who are unable to stop without it. We believe research should be done here to evaluate this. That is why we have made this one of the key smoking research priorities for the future, and we will be looking for well-structured proposals to come forward. This may well be a suitable area for joint funding with the pharmaceutical industry.

5.9 We will also support local NHS action with our new national public education campaign. Shifting young women's attitudes and behaviour on smoking will be a particularly important theme. As we develop the campaign we will build in tailored messages to highlight the importance of giving up smoking when pregnant.

During Pregnancy

5.10 Pregnancy is an ideal time for women and their partners who smoke to consider quitting; they are eager for information, have access to health services, and are often keen to make changes to their lifestyle. Most women are motivated to do what they can to make sure their baby is healthy. Often this can include wanting to stop smoking. The sooner the mother stops, the better for her own health, and that of her baby.

Pregnancy Quitline™

The Pregnancy Quitline pilot was launched in 1997 and is run by the charity Quit®, with joint NHS and commercial funding. Counsellors give callers information about the service, establish an on-going relationship, and agree a smoking cessation programme tailored directly to the needs of each individual. Contact between the counsellors and client may be more or less frequent depending on the level of support needed in each case. In its first year, Pregnancy Quitline has answered 3000 calls, (in addition to those made by counsellors to clients). 40 percent of clients are aged between 16 and 24, with half being referred by their GP or midwife. Evaluation is under way, but initial results are encouraging.

5.11 Midwives, GPs, obstetricians and other health professionals have regular, one-to-one contact with pregnant women. These contacts are ideal opportunities to offer support and practical advice on giving up smoking.

5.12 Evidence also shows that pre-natal counselling involving at least ten minutes person-to-person contact and written materials specifically designed for pregnant women, can double quit rates[41].

5.13 Women need specific and continuing support following the birth of their child. Health professionals can help by encouraging new mothers in their efforts to continue not smoking. For example, advice on breast feeding could include awareness that if the mother smokes, some nicotine will pass into the baby's bloodstream. Advice on how to reduce the risks of cot death could also include support with smoking cessation.

6 Smoking: action for everyone

6.1 The Government's strategy will focus on specific measures tailored towards the two key targets of reducing smoking among children and young people, and helping adults - especially the least advantaged - to give up smoking. But there are a number of important measures the Government will introduce which have wider application - cross-cutting measures which will help reduce smoking and so move towards the Government's goal of improving public health in Britain.

6.2 Building on the action the Government has already taken, including our policy on the taxation of tobacco, these cross-cutting steps include measures on:

- ending tobacco advertising

- changing attitudes

- tobacco smuggling

- research

Ending tobacco advertising

Why action is needed

6.3 Previous Governments have operated voluntary agreements with the tobacco industry on advertising. But there is little evidence that they have worked. Surveys show that 96 per cent of children say they have seen cigarette advertising in the last six months[9]. And smoking among the young has been rising for a number of years.

6.4 The cigarette brands smoked most by children are also those most heavily advertised[42]. Survey evidence shows that half of all young people believe they have seen a cigarette advert on TV in the last six

'96 per cent of children say they have seen cigarette advertising in the last six months'

months despite the fact that it was banned 33 years ago[9]. That suggests that tobacco sponsorship of televised events has a similar impact to direct advertising. The EC Directive phases out tobacco sponsorship and promotion as well as tobacco advertising on billboards and in printed media.

6.5   Most people want tobacco advertising to end. Sixty per cent of people believe that tobacco advertising should not be allowed at all. Even amongst smokers, 48 per cent agree. Fifty-two per cent of people disapprove of tobacco sponsorship of sports events, 63 per cent disapprove of tobacco sponsorship of pop concerts, and 58 per cent disapprove of tobacco sponsorship of arts events[32].

What we are going to do

6.6   The Government is now going to put the EC Directive into law in the UK - and into practice.

6.7   We will bring forward secondary legislation in the 1998/99 Parliamentary session[†], but before that we will consult on our plans. We intend to:

• end tobacco advertising on billboards and in the printed media at the earliest practicable opportunity

• require tobacco and non-tobacco products which share a brand name, trade mark, emblem or other distinctive feature, to be presented in a manner clearly distinct from each other from the date regulations come into force

• allow sports and arts the full five year period allowed under the Directive to find alternative sponsors. The Minister for Sport has already set up a group of sponsorship experts to help.

[†]The Scottish Parliament, to be established next year, may be in a position to implement the Directive separately in Scotland, as may the new Assemblies in Wales and Northern Ireland.

*'we intend to end
tobacco advertising
on billboards and in
the printed media at
the earliest practicable
opportunity'*

6.8 EU member states are free to implement the Directive within the timetable laid down within it. Now that the Directive has been adopted, Member States must by:

- **30 July 2001**   end most forms of tobacco advertising including billboards

- **30 July 2002**   end tobacco advertising in the press

- **30 July 2003**   end tobacco sponsorship other than of specified global events allowed to continue as special cases

- **30 July 2006**   end all tobacco sponsorship.

30 July 2006 is the date by which the Directive must be implemented in its entirety.

Billboards and printed media

6.9 The secondary legislation we introduce will end all tobacco advertising on billboards and in the printed media such as magazines at the earliest practicable opportunity, and well before the deadline required.

6.10 We see no strong reason to grant the printed media the additional year permissible. We want to avoid a situation in which the tobacco advertising money now spent on billboards gets shifted into printed advertising for a further year. The timetable will take account of the need to have in place satisfactory arrangements for implementation and enforcement.

Promotion and sponsorship

6.11 Our regulations will allow the extra time provided for under the Directive to phase out tobacco sponsorship of sports and other events. We recognise that sports and sports sponsors will need that sort of timescale to adjust. That is why we have always made it clear that we would only support the Directive if it made proper allowance for the time required by sports to find alternative sponsors. Experience overseas has shown that time is all that is needed in most cases for sponsored events to find other sources of funding.

6.12 Sponsorship of sport can best be sustained by sport itself establishing proper commercial links with business that sponsorship can be sustained. The Minister for Sport has set up a group of sponsorship experts under his chairmanship to offer support and guidance to sports who may need it. The approach is to help those sports help themselves by identifying what they have to offer sponsors in terms of access to markets, and by guiding them on professional practice and how best to make contact with businesses likely to be interested. The sports who have come forward include:

- rugby league

- clay pigeon shooting

- billiards and snooker

- pool

- darts

- ice hockey

- angling

We have also invited the Association for Business Sponsorship of the Arts to make representations on behalf of its members.

Global events

6.13 The EC Directive requires tobacco sponsorship of all sports events to be ended by July 2003. But it also provides for an extension to 2006 for global sporting events, subject to certain conditions.

'*sports and sports sponsors need time to adjust their businesses*'

6.14 Some sporting and arts events are global in character, including international football, international tennis and Formula One motor racing. Some global events have little or no dependence on tobacco sponsorship. Others have reduced their level of tobacco sponsorship. But some have yet to do so. Genuinely global sporting or arts events which are currently dependent on very high levels of tobacco sponsorship may find find it particularly difficult to adjust to alternative sponsorship. Global sports events with a high dependence on tobacco sponsorship will be given more time to adjust if they need it.

6.15 Formula One motor racing is different in structure to other global sports or arts events. World Cup football is an event in a single country every four years. International tennis is a series of different tournaments in a range of countries. By contrast, Formula One is a single competion spread across a large number of countries. So legal regulation of it is a much more complex proposal.

6.16 Formula One is believed to depend on around £35 million a year from sponsorship in the UK and around £100 million worldwide, a major part of which will be from the tobacco industry. It is simply not realistic to assume that this scale of investment can automatically be replaced for all teams within the general period allowed for sports generally.

6.17 That was why we argued along with other EU member states for a clause in the Directive which would allow individual member states to continue to authorise existing sponsorship of global events for three years more than other sporting events in exceptional cases. In allowing this, the Directive requires the sums involved in the sponsorship to diminish over the extended period and that the visible advertising also reduces. So in order to be eligible for a longer period of adjustment until 2006 Formula One racing will have to demonstrate by 2003 at the latest that it is complying with these requirements.

6.18 We could have taken action ourselves to end tobacco sponsorship of Formula One in Britain. But it would have been ineffective, since Formula One races in the rest of Europe and around the world would still have been seen on television in the UK. Despite this, such action might have run the risk of damaging the British motor sports industry. Britain is particularly successful in Formula One racing, with a large majority of competing cars manufactured in the UK. Many successful teams operate from the UK. Britain forms a key industrial cluster point in this international sport. Formula One is a popular sport in Britain, with a significant following. Britain's success in Formula One is a considerable national asset.

6.19 Instead we negotiated with our EU partners for European-wide action. As a result, by 2006 at the latest, Formula One will have to have ended all its tobacco sponsorship to comply with the terms of the Directive. This change will eliminate tobacco advertising on television screens from all European Formula One events.

6.20 However, Formula One may not need to make use of all the available extended period. In March 1998, the sport's organising body, the FIA, made a public announcement that "if presented with evidence of a direct link between tobacco advertising/sponsorship and smoking, it would act to eliminate tobacco advertising/sponsorship from Formula One". The FIA indicated that this could mean a world-wide ban on tobacco advertising/sponsorship at Formula One events from 2002. Britain and others have provided evidence which the FIA is now studying. We look forward to the outcome of that process and would welcome the complete elimination of tobacco sponsorship from Formula One events anywhere in the world. This change would eliminate tobacco advertising from Formula One on television screens in the UK and across Europe from races staged outside the EU.

'this change will eliminate tobacco advertising on television screens from all European Formula One events'

Brand-stretching

6.21 Brand-stretching means taking a name already established for one type of product and using it for a quite different type of product. When this happens, the advertising of each product indirectly promotes the other because they share a brand in common. This has happened with many brands, including well-known tobacco brands.

'we will monitor developments to ensure that this exemption is not used by tobacco companies to circumvent the ban'

6.22 Some tobacco companies may be drawn towards 'stretching' their brands in the face of the phasing out of tobacco advertising. Non-tobacco products might be launched with a tobacco product brand name, logo or other distinctive feature, or a tobacco product might be introduced using a brand name already used for a non-tobacco product.

6.23 The EC Directive lays down provisions which will make it illegal to advertise tobacco products indirectly using other products. A tobacco product's brand name or branding features may be used on a non-tobacco product, but only if the presentation and the advertising of the non-tobacco product are clearly distinct from those of the tobacco product.

6.24 Member states may allow a tobacco brand name which is being used in good faith for non-tobacco products or services traded prior to 30th July 1998 to be used for the advertising of those other goods or services.

6.25 While we are committed to ending tobacco advertising, we want to minimise the impact on non-tobacco businesses. Our legislation will as far as possible allow the businesses involved time to make the necessary changes to the presentation and advertising of their products. The industries involved have already made representations to the Government. We are keen to hear their views again on implementation issues.

Direct marketing

6.26 All direct and indirect tobacco advertising and promotion will be phased out, including the distribution of free cigarettes, cigarette coupon schemes and other brand loyalty incentive schemes. Such schemes and activities encourage smokers to keep on smoking.

6.27 As required by the Directive, we will outlaw any form of commercial communication which has the aim or effect of promoting a tobacco product.

Other areas

6.28 The Directive does not apply in the following areas:

- *communications intended exclusively for professionals in the tobacco trade.* This means communications not intended for the public, but which are necessary to the conduct of the tobacco trade. Examples might include product and price brochures for retailers; wholesale order forms, invoices and receipts; tobacco duty and import export documentation. This will be further defined in the legislation

- *the presentation of tobacco products offered for sale and the indication of their prices at tobacco sales outlets*

- *advertising aimed at purchasers in establishments specialising in the sale of tobacco products and on their shop-fronts or, in the case of establishments selling a variety of articles or services, at locations reserved for the sale of tobacco products...".* We are taking action in this area (see Chapter Three).

- *the sale of publications containing advertising for tobacco products which are published and printed in third countries, where those publications are not primarily intended for the Community market.* While the general press will be covered by the legislation, there is a case for exempting publications produced outside the EU and whose main market lies outside the EU. We will monitor developments to ensure that this exemption is not used by tobacco companies to circumvent the ban.

6.29 We have a choice in each of these areas of whether or not to introduce our own controls to lay down stricter provisions where necessary for health protection.

Consultation

'we said we would consult fully on the implementation of our manifesto commitment. We are keeping that promise'

6.30 We said we would consult fully on the implementation of our manifesto commitment. We are keeping that promise, and will continue to do so. As we prepare draft legislation, we will further update a regulatory impact assessment (RIA) which includes an employment impact assessment. The current draft of the RIA is published today as a stand alone document. Requests for further copies and comments should be sent to the Department of Health, Wellington House, 133-155 Waterloo Road, London SE1 8UG by the end of February 1999.

Enforcement

6.31 A number of agencies are likely to be involved in monitoring the advertising ban, particularly local authority Trading Standards Officers. We will be involving them in detailed discussions as we prepare to legislate.

6.32 Individuals or organisations with a legitimate interest may be able to bring suspected breaches to the attention of trading standards authorities.

6.33 Proposed penalties for breaches of the law will be contained in the draft legislation

Changing attitudes

6.34 Public education programmes are the most direct way of changing attitudes and behaviour, and an essential component in any strategy designed to combat smoking.

Research evidence

6.35 Other countries which have taken action over smoking, such as the USA and Norway, have found large scale and sustained public education campaigns to be vital. In California, the Californian *Tobacco Control Program* which started in 1989 has been the subject of much evaluation. A recent study showed that in 1996, smoking prevalence in California was 18 per cent compared with 22 per cent in the rest of the United States. The study's authors commented:

The California Tobacco Control Program has confirmed the findings from earlier studies that large health promotion programmes can have a major influence on smoking behaviour[12].

The study also observed that the impact was greater at the start of the programme than more recently, and identified reduced programme funding as a possible reason.

The importance of dynamic health education programmes is acknowledged elsewhere too. The Norwegian Health Minister, commenting on the positive impact of Norway's advertising ban, said:

The effect could have been even better if the ban had been accompanied by a much more active and offensive use of other smoking control measures, in particular, health information and education[43].

6.36 In the UK, research reinforces the approach. In 1992, the Health Education Authority began a two-year controlled trial to test the effectiveness of mass media and local support activity in changing smoking attitudes and behaviour. Varying intensities of mass media advertising and local activity were tried in three television regions in the north of England, while a fourth control region had no media or other activity. The final evaluation is due to be published in the near future. However, indicative results suggest that an integrated mass media campaign has a significant positive effect on smoking prevalence. In particular, the study suggests that:

'adequately funded health education programmes as part of a comprehensive strategy and with sustained funding have a lasting effect on smoking behaviour'

- television advertising made the main contribution to changing smoking behaviour

- nationwide replication of the advertising alone might have produced a reduction in smoking prevalence of 1.2 per cent

- nationally, this would have led to about 100,000 smokers quitting for good[44].

What action are we taking?

6.37 Adequately funded health education programmes as part of a comprehensive strategy and with sustained funding have a lasting effect on smoking behaviour.

6.38 We are committing some £50 million over the next three years to develop a sustained and co-ordinated new campaign[†]. This is far more than the previous Government was prepared to invest and is, we believe, the level of funding needed to make a real and lasting impact.

Priority groups

6.39 In line with our target aims, young people and adults who want to quit - especially the disadvantaged, and pregnant women who smoke- will be a prime focus.

[†]Resources for health education on smoking will be made available over three years in England (£50m), Scotland (£5m), and Northern Ireland (£1m). Funding in Wales is subject to the outcome of the Comprehensive Spending Review in Wales.

6.40 The campaign aimed at young people will persuade them to think twice before smoking. As we phase out tobacco advertising, health-related messages will make a greater impact. For years, tobacco companies have spent millions on advertising. Now we are prepared to do the same. The types of media used, and the style and design, must be relevant to the target audience and informed by marketing and advertising campaigns which have a proven track record of success with this group. Teenage magazines will play an important role, and we will continue to collaborate with their editors in getting our messages across.

6.41 Adult smokers who want to quit, particularly the less well-off, will also be a focus of effort. Our new campaign will include advertising and other media activity, targeted particularly at smokers in worse-off social groups. It will encourage them to stop smoking by presenting the benefits of quitting, e.g. feeling fitter and having more money to spend. It will offer help and advice in sustaining a decision to stop smoking, and point to local NHS smoking cessation services for practical support. Education and support is also important for smokers who use NRT as a cessation aid. We will explore the scope for collaborative working with professional bodies representing pharmacies and pharmacists, as well as the manufacturers of nicotine replacement therapy.

6.42 We will develop programmes to inform and motivate women who smoke and who are planning to have children to give up. The national campaign will include materials specifically designed for this audience. Active support will also be developed through our NHS smoking cessation services, and health professionals who come into contact with expectant mothers, particularly midwives, will have a key role to play.

6.43 Our education campaign will also target a wider public with messages which create a climate of support for smoke-free policies and, in particular, for smoke-free public and work places.

'teenage magazines will play an important role'

6.44 This is a major new initiative. We will be working up more detailed plans in the coming months.

West Yorkshire Smoking and Health (WYSH)

The aim of WYSH is to help reduce smoking and provide information on smoking issues by boosting local activities, using the media and promoting debate. Local organisations trying to reduce smoking include Bradford Stubs It Out, Calderdale Calls It Quits, Kirklees Smoke-Free, Leeds Breathing Space, Wakefield Smoking Task Group and Yorkshire ASH. WYSH has developed packs for doctors and practice nurses called "Smoking in a Nutshell" and "Smoking Cessation in Practice" in order to help them help people who want to stop smoking. They also publish the Yorkshire Guide to Smoke-Free Air, which includes places with the Roy Castle Good Air Award.

Local involvement

6.45 We will be looking to key local players including schools, health authorities, local authorities, businesses, and voluntary and youth groups to work together to support the national campaigns. There are already some 25 "local alliances" operating around the country for example in Birmingham.

6.46 Teachers and school nurses will continue to provide education on the dangers of smoking at successive key stages. The Healthy Schools Initiative, jointly run by the Department for Education and Employment (DfEE) and the Department of Health (DH), will include anti-smoking education in national criteria for membership of the Health Schools Award Scheme. Good practice guidance on tobacco and other drug education will be issued shortly.

[†]In Scotland, guidance, advice and materials are already available.

Smoke-Free Birmingham

Smoke-Free Birmingham is an example of a high profile local alliance. It is run from a local NHS Trust and benefits from the skills and influence of the health authority, local authority, local businesses, schools, voluntary groups, sports clubs and individuals. It is able to co-ordinate comprehensive local action to help reduce smoking. It:

- provides smoking cessation training for local health professionals

- promotes national initiatives such as the telephone quitline through local press advertising, leafleting, competitions and events

- distributes information to local employers on workplace smoking policies

- works with local media to produce a guide to smoke-free places in Birmingham

- works with local professional sports clubs to promote a healthy non-smoking lifestyle to local children

- works closely with the local trading standards office to prevent sales of cigarettes to under-16s

6.47 In addition, an advisory group has been set up by DfEE and DH to develop a national framework for personal, social and health education in schools and to consider its relationship to other curriculum areas. It will include a focus on enabling pupils to acquire the necessary skills to resist pressure to take up smoking[†]. The work of the Government's Women's Unit on teenage girls, recently announced by the Minister for Women, may also identify further action we can take to reduce self-damaging activities such as smoking amongst this vulnerable group.

6.48 Parents and those who work with children and young people can play an important part in the prevention of smoking by children and young people and supporting those who wish to give up.

Monitoring impact

6.49 It is our intention that this campaign will not only be the biggest, but the most carefully constructed and monitored anti-smoking campaign ever mounted by Government. Evaluation will be a fundamental feature. We will not only monitor general awareness of the campaign among the target audience, but more particularly we will test its impact on their attitudes. We will listen carefully to how they react, to what they say about smoking, and how far they intend to change, or have already changed, their behaviour.

Anti-smuggling drive

Why action is needed

'*smuggling is a crime. It can be punished with a fine, or a 7 year prison term*'

6.50 The Government's policy of increasing tobacco duty by on average 5 per cent a year in real terms will help to encourage smokers to cut down or quit, and will help to discourage other children and adults from starting. But the effectiveness of continued tax increases is being undermined by tobacco smuggling. As we have continued to raise tobacco tax in the UK, the potential profit that smugglers can make from the differential between our tobacco prices and those elsewhere in the EU has grown. The availability of cheaper tobacco, whether legitimately purchased abroad or smuggled, is undermining to a degree the health goal of our tobacco taxation strategy.

6.51 Smuggling is a crime. It can be punished with a fine, or a 7 year prison term. The total revenue lost on unpaid tobacco duty was £1 billion in 1997/98 about 9.5 per cent of the total amount of duty and VAT collected on tobacco in the 1997/98 financial year.

6.52 The growth in tobacco smuggling is a major cause for concern, but cutting duty rates is not the answer since it would increase the number of smokers. Indeed, some countries with much lower duty rates than the UK, such as Italy and Spain, suffer high levels of penetration of their legitimate market by smuggling.

6.53 By evading UK tobacco taxes, smugglers are in a position to charge lower prices than reputable shopkeepers and still make large profits. Because smugglers operate outside the law, they may well be prepared to sell tobacco to children, and that is a particular cause for concern. What is worse, much smuggled tobacco is in the form of hand rolling tobacco which tends to have the highest tar content of all tobacco.

What we are doing

6.54 In his July 1997 Budget, the Chancellor announced that HM Customs and Excise would carry out a review into alcohol and tobacco fraud and smuggling. Trade Associations and other interested parties were consulted and practical solutions to the problem were developed. The outcome was reported in July this year as part of the Government's Comprehensive Spending Review.

6.55 As a result, £35 million is being made available to Customs over the next three financial years to mount a new offensive against smuggling. Resources are available in this financial year so that Customs can begin implementing the strategy.

6.56 An extra 100 staff, specially trained to fight fraud and smuggling, will be brought in. The new Customs staff will concentrate their efforts on areas of greatest risk to enable continued improvements in detection rates. There will be measures to tackle paper based fraud, such as falsifying export documentation for cigarettes which are instead illegally diverted for sale in the UK. Customs will also work closely with other enforcement agencies such as the police and the Benefits Agency, and with the tobacco and alcohol industries to tighten control over the movement of excise goods on which no duty has been paid. These measures complement a tougher prosecution policy adopted earlier this year which involves urging the courts to use all available sanctions including driving disqualifications, compensation orders for lost revenue, vehicle confiscation orders and revocation of haulage and liquor licenses.

6.57 We have left the level of duty on hand rolling tobacco unchanged in the last two Budgets to reduce the incentive to smuggle.

6.58 An example of UK Customs' pro-active approach is the current "Operation Mistletoe". It involves targeting the busy pre-Christmas period during which more smuggled goods are sold including tobacco. Visits to retail premises are made by Customs, illegal goods are seized and then prosecutions sought. Such action disrupts the illegal trade and protects honest shopkeepers.

6.59 But the problem of smuggling and excise fraud is not unique to the UK. The heads of EU Customs and Indirect Tax administrations around Europe have been discussing ways to address the problems of both tobacco and alcohol fraud on an EU-wide basis. They have made recommendations, accepted by the EU's European Council of Economic and Finance Ministers (ECOFIN) in May 1998, which complement those of our own Fraud Review. UK Customs are now working closely with their EU counterparts to implement the proposals.

6.60 Our immediate objective is to reduce the rate of growth of smuggling. The new Customs staff will concentrate their efforts on areas of greatest risk to enable continued improvement in detection rates.

Research

6.61 The Department of Health will be giving high priority to research into smoking when commissioning future research. Further research is needed on:

- the safety of nicotine replacement therapy (NRT) when used during pregnancy by women who cannot quit but who want to minimise the harm to their babies

- the safety and effectiveness of NRT: when used as an aid to smoking less (to reduce exposure to the harm caused by tobacco smoke); when used over long periods of time; and when used by children

- identifying the most effective method of helping different groups of smokers to quit (e.g. school children; pregnant women; lone parents) and in different settings (e.g. GP surgery; pharmacy; hospital; school)

- the effectiveness of cutting down the amount of tobacco smoked over a period of time as a way of leading up to quitting rather than stopping altogether in the first instance

- evaluating key aspects of the policies set out in this White Paper in order to assess the effectiveness and health impact of this package, e.g. the health education campaign and the new NHS services

- the relationship between the brand of tobacco smoked and the nicotine exposure.

7 Clean air

7.1 People are increasingly insisting on a healthy environment and clean air. Forward-looking businesses are already providing it for both their customers and staff. Public attitudes have changed a lot over the last two decades. Smoke-filled buses, trains and cinemas are a fading memory. Businesses that fail to recognise this will increasingly find customers voting with their feet. The vast majority of people agree that smoking should be restricted in public places. Forty-two per cent of people already take the availability of a non-smoking area into account when choosing a restaurant, and 1 in 5 people already do so when choosing a pub[32]. Provision is improving, but there is a long way to go.

Telford Shopping Centre

Chris Crane, Customer Services and Promotions Manager at Telford shopping centre said of their change to a no-smoking environment:

"The majority of comments and letters received from our customers about our no-smoking policy are extremely supportive. Parents of young children can now shop safely without the fear of their children being burnt by cigarettes in crowded areas, and can enjoy the benefits of clean healthy air. Our customer traffic has increased substantially since the policy was introduced - our traders are delighted and fully support the policy. We are proud to display our Roy Castle Gold Award to reinforce our commitment to smoke-free air."

7.2 We want to build on the progress of recent years. At present, non-smokers are often exposed to the health risks, discomfort and irritation of tobacco smoke, while smokers often get forced to smoke on the street. The friction and aggravation felt by smokers and non-smokers alike is the result of a lack of proper choice.

Passive smoking

7.3 The health risks are clear. Passive smoking does carry risks but they are small compared to the risks of active smoking. A non-smoker, living or working in a very smoky environment over a prolonged period, is 20-30 per cent more likely to get cancer than a non-smoker who does not[20]. Hundreds of people die every year in the UK as a result of high levels of exposure to passive smoke.

7.4 We do not think a universal ban on smoking in all public places is justified while we can make fast and substantial progress in partnership with industry.

7.5 We have looked very carefully at the case for an outright ban, or legal restrictions, like the ones tried in some other countries. A number of countries have tried an outright ban on smoking in bars and restaurants. But such restrictions have proved difficult to implement. We want to work with business and others to achieve real change, highlighting and building on best practice. In public places we want to see real choice for the public as a whole - non-smokers and smokers.

7.6 We agree that completely smoke-free places are the ideal, and some businesses have taken the decision to go completely smoke-free. We support them in their decision, and would like to see more. But we recognise that it is not always going to be possible. So the next best thing is separate rooms for those who want to smoke, and for those who do not want to smoke. If they cannot be provided, separate areas are the next best thing, with good ventilation and air cleaning, so that the atmosphere is more comfortable for everyone.

'we want to work with business and others to achieve real change'

7.7   The hospitality industry - pubs, restaurants, hotels - recognises that consumers expect not to have to socialise in smoky atmospheres if they do not want to. Hospitality businesses know it makes good business sense to provide what customers want. There is clear scope for further development through partnership, with Government working together with the industry to find the best solutions.

Promoting smoke free areas in pubs

Easy Breathing project, Bristol

Many customers want to choose non-smoking facilities, and guides for restaurants/pubs providing smoke-free areas for diners are proving popular. This is not necessarily just non-smokers, but also smokers may prefer to eat in a smoke-free environment. One such guide is the Bristol "Easy Breathing" project, which has signed up a large number of pubs to provide a smoke-free area.

7.8   Gradual improvements in the provision of non-smoking facilities in public and work places have been made over a period of decades. But while progress is being made generally, it is not consistent across the board. Policies tend to be best in education and health establishments, and many large employers have made their workplaces primarily smoke-free with appropriate provision for smokers. Progress has been slower among smaller employers and leisure establishments such as pubs, clubs and restaurants.

7.9   Consumers deserve to know they have a choice to make and to be able to exercise it. Staff have a right to choose not to work in smoky conditions. New legislation is not necessary if owners and employers recognise these points and act accordingly.

7.10 Ultimately, it is the responsibility of all of us as individuals, employees, consumers and employers to drive change in public places generally. Our health and comfort are at stake.

Smoking in public places

7.11 Seven out of ten people do not smoke. Those people should not have to breathe other people's smoke when they go into a pub or restaurant if they do not wish to. On the other hand, if someone who smokes wants to spend the evening in a pub with friends who either smoke themselves, or who do not mind other people's smoke, they should be able to do so. It is a question of balance. But most people think more should be done to restrict smoking in public places[32]. The Government is taking action which reflects that.

What action are we taking?

7.12 We have reached agreement with representatives of the licensed hospitality trade that there is a need for continuing improvement in the provision of non-smoking facilities over the coming years. We will now negotiate with them to work up the detail of a Charter which will ensure that consumers are better able to choose whether to eat, drink or socialise in smoky atmospheres.

7.13 The Charter we have agreed is sensible, practical and will deliver real improvements. Pubs, bars and even restaurants are widely acknowledged to be particularly difficult places in which to address the issue of smoking. We congratulate the industry and welcome its approach. Now we look to further members of the licensed trade, such as the Scottisch Licensed Trade Association (SLTA), and members of the non-licensed trade, such as guest houses, cafes and fast-food outlets, to follow suit.

'pubs, bars and even restaurants are widely acknowledged to be particularly difficult places in which to address the issue of smoking'

7.14 We have agreed with bodies representing the hospitality trade the following principles, which will be worked up in detail in due course with targets to be achieved over agreed timescales:

Association of Licensed Multiple Retailers (ALMR)

Brewers and Licensed Retailers Association (BLRA)

British Institute of Innkeeping

Public Places Charter

The signatories to this Charter recognise that non-smoking is the general norm and that there should be increasing provision of facilities for non-smokers and the availability of clean air. The signatories therefore commit themselves in principle to achieving the following objectives in premises for which they are responsible or which they represent:

1. A written policy on smoking, available to customers and staff

2. Implementation through non-smoking areas, air cleaning and ventilation, as appropriate and whenever practicable

3. Communication to customers through external signage to an agreed format and appropriate internal signs

4. Implementation on a rolling basis over a number of years, informed by an initial assessment of the current position, internal monitoring and subsequent independent research to monitor progress

5. Recognition of smoking policies as a management responsibility to be reflected in general training, qualification and supervision

6. Support for shared expertise and guidance on commercial and technical benefits of smoking policies and air cleaning.

The Government applauds these aims and will encourage and support the signatories in achieving them.

British Hospitality Association (BHA)

Restaurant Association

7.15 We will be working closely with the industry to turn the principles of the Charter into practical action on the ground.

7.16 Independent research will be funded by the industry, but commissioned in conjunction with the Department of Health, to monitor progress against agreed target improvements.

7.17 Individual complaints not resolvable through the businesses or representative bodies concerned would be matters for trading standards or other enforcement routes as appropriate.

7.18 Progress towards the targets will be monitored, and if necessary the targets will be reviewed, on a regular basis between the representative bodies concerned and the Department of Health.

7.19 Training in smoking policy issues will become a requirement for the National Licensee Certificate provided by the British Institute of Innkeeping. The Institute issues 30,000 such certificates each year and magistrates are increasingly expecting applicants for liquor licenses to have qualified for the certificate.

7.20 With pubs, bars and restaurants displaying notices outside the premises informing customers of the type of smoking policy in operation within the building, non-smokers will be able to choose whether to expose themselves to the health risks and discomfort associated with passive smoking. Consumer choice will continue to drive the progress that the public wants in the provision of smoke-free areas in public places.

7.21 We have agreed in principle with the industry that there should be a national industry-led scheme to badge restaurants, pubs and bars with an agreed symbol denoting the type of smoking policy in operation inside. Consumers will then be in a position to choose which establishment to enter on the basis of its smoking policy. Consumers can do a lot by simply asking for smoke-free areas to be provided as well as by voting with their feet. Local health promotion units and voluntary groups compile lists of places with smoke-free accommodation.

'consumers can do a lot by simply asking for smoke-free areas to be provided'

7.22 Customers are famililiar with hospitality premises being evaluated by the number of symbols displayed, with the best-rated establishments given five, the next-best four, and so on. While the categories of smoking policy have yet to be agreed with the industries concerned, we think there are five key levels which should be indicated in any system if customers are to be able to make a real choice:

- Non-smoking No smoking allowed at any time

- Separated Smoking and non-smoking areas are separated by walls

- Designated Areas with spaces clearly defined for smoking and non-smoking

- Ventilated Non-defined areas but special ventilation equipment used to improve comfort for non-smokers

- Smoking No segregation or special ventilation equipment

7.23 Ventilation systems can improve the comfort and welfare of the public and employees. The best systems can, provided they are properly operated and maintained, protect non-smokers from exposure to carcinogens. However, without being able to guarantee that such equipment is maintained and operated properly, we cannot endorse it as being as effective as smoke-free areas. We are already in discussion with manufacturers of air-cleaning equipment through the *Atmosphere Improves Results (AIR)* industry initiative on the development of agreed standards for equipment which we can endorse.

Smoking at work

What action are we taking?

7.24 We are not going to ban smoking at work. But the Health and Safety Commission (HSC) is going to consult on a new Approved Code of Practice on smoking in the workplace. This will considerably toughen existing measures. The Code will be designed to improve protection of the welfare of all employees by defining the kind of smoking policies employers need to operate to comply with existing health & safety legislation. Consultation will begin in Spring 1999.

What is an Approved Code of Practice?

7.25 An Approved Code of Practice is a form of guidance. It gives practical advice on how to comply with the law. If employers follow the advice they will be doing enough to comply with the law in respect of those specific matters on which the Code gives advice. They may use alternative methods to those set out in the Code in order to comply with the law.

7.26 The content of the Approved Code of Practice, if agreed, would be based on the content of the existing guidance from the Health and Safety Executive (HSE)[45], so that employers should:

- introduce smoking policies that give priority to the needs of non-smoking employees, whether the smoke comes from other employees or from customers

- take special care for people who have a health condition that may be made worse by tobacco smoke

'policies that give priority to the needs of non-smoking employees'

7.27 Approved Codes of Practice have a special status under the Health and Safety at Work etc. Act 1974. Although it is not of itself an offence to fail to comply with the provisions of a Code, if an employer is prosecuted for a breach of health, safety and welfare law, and it is proved that they did not follow the relevant provisions of the Code, they need to show that they have complied with the law in some other way, or a Court will find them at fault.

7.28 Health and safety inspectors from the HSE and Local Authorities would be able to quote a Code on smoking in the workplace in court in cases of alleged breaches of the Health and Safety at Work. Act. In practice, this would put the burden of proof on employers, making the new Code significantly stronger than existing guidance which is entirely voluntary.

Consultation

7.29 Details of the likely effect of the Code will depend on its content which will be set out in detail in a consultation document to be released by the HSC in Spring 1999. The HSC covers England, Scotland and Wales. Similar action will be taken by the Health and Safety Executive for Northern Ireland. In Scotland, close consultation will take place with the Health at Work Awards Scheme, which develops and implements workplace policies.

Workplace smoking cessation

7.30 Good employers are beginning to offer their staff help if they want to give up smoking. Seven out of ten smokers say they want to give up, and employers who help them do so are likely to find a healthier, fitter workforce, and fewer days missed through illness. Employers can help by:

- arranging group counselling workshops run by trained health professionals

- using educational materials made available as part of national anti-smoking campaigns

- getting involved in local initiatives involving the health authority or other groups

Kendall Company UK Ltd., Cornwall

Some employers are already offering their staff help to quit smoking. For example, to help those of his employees who wanted to quit, the Plant Director of Kendall Company UK Ltd. in Cornwall provides free nicotine replacement therapy patches to his employees. The employees sign a personal contract with the company to pay back the costs of the patches if they start smoking again. The scheme continues to enable employees of Kendalls to quit smoking.

Government offices

What are we going to do?

7.31 Most Government Departments are making a specific policy contribution to the package of measures in this white paper - this document is very much about joined-up government. But we are determined that every Department should also take practical steps to set a good example to other sectors. All Departments will be conducting full reviews of their internal office smoking policies. Policies will be expected to reflect the content of any new HSC Approved Code of Practice.

'all departments will be conducting full reviews of their internal office smoking policies'

7.32 Each Department will be responsible for taking forward its own review. The Department of Health will monitor progress to see that they have been carried out and implemented.

7.33 The NHS Executive has recently reviewed smoking policies in the NHS in England. It has found that virtually all hospitals have smoking policies, but that not all are properly in operation. The NHS Executive will be providing advice in the form of a "tool-kit" to help the NHS ensure its policies are put into practice. Similar initiatives are under way elsewhere in the UK.

8 Smoking and international action

8.1 There are over a billion smokers across the world. Nearly one third of smokers are in China. Smoking is fast increasing in third world countries and in Eastern Europe. Smoking now causes 3 million deaths a year worldwide. If trends continue, there will be 10 million deaths from smoking worldwide in about 30 years' time[13].

8.2 The effects of tobacco are increasingly taking their toll across the world. Many of the countries in which smoking is increasing fast have limited regulation of tobacco or health education and health care systems which are ill-equipped to handle the consequences. In parts of Africa tobacco companies are using advertising and marketing campaigns, sponsorship of events and price wars to promote cut-priced tobacco[46].

8.3 We, in concert with other Governments, can take steps to counter the global trend. It is important that we provide strong support. Smoking kills around the world; we need action around the world.

European action

a) Pressure for EU tobacco tax changes

What are we going to do?

8.4 The Government opposes harmonisation of tax rates across the EU. The Government will only agree to any tax changes where it is in the interests of Britain to do so. The Government is pursuing a clear policy in the UK over the taxation of tobacco.

8.5 We would like our fellow member states to agree to increase the minimum levels of duty which apply across the EU. Such a step would be to the benefit of public health across the EU, and would reduce the scope for profit to be made by smuggling tobacco into the UK from other EU countries. We cannot achieve this without the agreement of our EU partners, who will retain the right to veto any such changes - as Britain does with proposals from other EU member states.

8.6   We will continue to argue our case and to persuade our EU partners. Specifically, we would like to agree the following changes with them:

- significant increases in the minimum rates of duty on all tobacco products

- the introduction of a cash minimum duty for cigarettes

- an increase in the upper limit for the flat rate ("specific") component of duty on cigarettes

8.7   This final change would help enable us to avoid making tobacco tax increases in the form of proportional ("ad valorem") duty. Increases in ad valorem duty are less effective because they widen the price range of cigarettes on the market, encouraging smokers to switch to cheaper but equally unhealthy brands rather than to cut down or, preferably, quit altogether.

'reduce the scope for profit to be made by smuggling tobacco into the UK from other EU countries'

How will we go about this?

8.8   Periodically, the European Commission reviews the structure and rates of excise duties on tobacco products. The second such review took place in May this year. The Commission's proposals failed to address our concerns. The Commission proposed only relatively minor technical amendments to the tax rules. We have registered our dissatisfaction with these proposals by reserving the UK's position, and will seek to overcome their shortcomings in the light of wider EU tax discussions and the reactions of other member states.

8.9   Whatever we manage to agree at an EU level, we will continue to press the health case for high tobacco duties with our EU partners. But we recognise that progress on these issues may only be possible in the longer term.

b) European action on labelling

8.10 The European Commission is currently examining possible improvements to the existing directives governing the labelling of tobacco products, and the tar and nicotine content of tobacco. We are keen to help the Commission develop effective, practical proposals.

8.11 Given the single market approach taken by the EU on tobacco labelling, packaging, taxation and now advertising, we believe it is sensible for developments in the regulation of tobacco products within the EU to continue to be pursued on a European-wide basis.

8.12 At the conclusion of the Council of Health Ministers meeting on 4 December 1997, the European Commission was asked to bring forward new proposals for tobacco products in the areas of tar, nicotine and labelling. We welcome the fact that the Commission are working on proposals, and believe that the Commission review should take account of developments outside the EU. For example, Canada and Australia have introduced larger, more prominent health warnings on cigarette packets. Moreover, almost 600 chemical additives can be used in tobacco products, but there is no requirement for tobacco manufacturers to disclose which ones they actually use. This differs from food additives, which must be disclosed on packaging.

8.13 Commissioner Flynn has said that possible measures in the forthcoming EU proposals could cover tar, nicotine and carbon monoxide levels, labelling requirements, and further information on additives and other non-tobacco ingredients.

Responding for the UK at the Health Council on the 12 November 1998, Public Health Minister Tessa Jowell said:

The UK believes such rules are best made at Community level, in view of the single market in tobacco products within the EU. The UK looks forward to seeing formal proposals in due course. We are keen to work constructively with our fellow Member States, and with the Commission, to arrive at sound practical rules which will work.

'we are keen to help the Commission develop effective, practical proposals'

c) Agricultural policy reform

8.14 There is an EU support regime for tobacco under the Common Agricultural Policy in which tobacco growers, mainly in the southern Member States, are paid for growing tobacco up to specified production levals (quotas). Much of the tobacco grown is of poor quality and is therefore exported to countries outside the EU. UK taxpayers contribute to the cost of the system.

8.15 We have consistently argued that the EU policy on tobacco growing is out of step with others such as the recently agreed Directive on tobacco advertising. In June 1998, under the UK Presidency, a number of changes were agreed to the tobacco regime. From the 1999 harvest, tobacco growers wishing to leave the sector must offer their quota allocation to other producers. If the allocation is not bought by other producers, growers will receive a payment under the regime for the quota given up. A further change will be an increase in the funding of the Community Tobacco Fund which supports research, for example, into the effects of smoking and alternative ways for tobacco farmers to make a living.

'an increase in the funding of the Community Tobacco Fund which supports research'

8.16 The "quota buy-back" scheme, as it is known, should result in a reduction in the total amount of subsidised tobacco production in the EU over a number of years. The Commission is due to report on the working of the revised regime by 1 April 2002.

Worldwide action

a) World health campaigning

8.17 We will continue to work with other Governments towards a global ban on tobacco advertising. In the meantime we will support an international code of conduct for trans-national companies advertising products, covering the content and exposure of children to advertising, and the use of health warnings.

'we will do everything we can to help, drawing on our experience of tackling tobacco'

8.18 We will ensure that our development assistance funds are not used for any purpose which identifiably supports the tobacco sector in aid recipient countries. At the same time, funding in these countries can be provided to help reduce tobacco dependence as well as to help farmers dependent on tobacco crops to diversify into alternative activities.

8.19 We will provide support to the World Health Organisation's (WHO) long term mission to decrease global tobacco consumption. WHO's Tobacco-free Initiative is aiming, by 2001, to make smoking issues a global concern and provide leadership to strengthen international anti-smoking action.

8.20 A major component of this initiative is the development of an International Framework Convention (IFC) on tobacco control, intended to enable and encourage countries to strengthen their national tobacco strategies. The IFC will set out detailed evidence-based advice on the range of measures which a country wishing to take action on smoking could usefully include in its strategy. The IFC is expected to be presented to the World Health Assembly in 2003. The WHO is already mobilising advocacy, technical and financial support which will help spread the IFC around the world.

8.21 We welcome the priority that the new Director General of the WHO, Dr Gro Harlem Brundtland, is giving to tobacco issues and in particular the proposal to develop an IFC. Dr Brundtland has asked the UK to take a leading part in developing the IFC. We will do everything we can to help, drawing on our experience of tackling tobacco, and will be discussing with the WHO how we can most effectively be involved in this landmark initiative. We hope that the package of measures in this White Paper will play an important part in helping to develop its content.

8.22 The WHO also has a specific strategy for tackling smoking in Europe which it calls an Action Plan for a Tobacco-Free Europe. We support the aims of this initiative and are of the view that co-operation on anti-tobacco work by non-EU countries should be viewed positively when they are preparing to join the EU early in the next century.

b) Role of British posts overseas

8.23 Smoking rates are growing around the world. UK tobacco firms are exporting increasingly large quantities of tobacco products overseas.

8.24 We are not in the business of banning the production or export of tobacco products, and the Department of Trade and Industry (DTI) and our embassies and high commissions will continue to provide advice, to which UK companies are entitled, in the sale of legal products. However, in keeping with the current practice of Ministers and officials not becoming involved in the advertising or promotion of tobacco products at home, guidelines will shortly be issued to representatives in our diplomatic posts instructing them to be scrupulous to ensure that they follow suit overseas, taking into account local circumstances.

9 Judging success

'we will set targets for smoking cessation services in the NHS'

9.1 We will judge the success of this White Paper by measuring our performance against three challenging targets, on children smoking, adults smoking and smoking during pregnancy. These targets are all set for the year 2010. However, as smoking is a key cause of cancer and circulatory disease (two of the four priority areas in *Our Healthier Nation*) the targets also include an indication of where we expect to be by the year 2005 to check on progress. We have decided to keep the number of high-level targets small to concentrate attention on the most important areas. These targets are for England: separate targets are being set in Scotland, Wales and Northern Ireland.

9.2 We will also be monitoring progress in a number of other areas to check how the measures are working. In particular, we will set targets for smoking cessation services in the NHS, and will be looking for improvements in the provision of smoke-free areas in public places.

Children smoking

9.3 Our immediate aim is to halt the rise in children smoking, and then to see reductions in smoking levels over time. This is the most challenging area. It is also essential if we are to re-establish the downward trend in adult smoking levels in the future, and secure the continued decline in cancer and heart disease deaths in generations to come. We will be looking closely at the level of smoking among 15-year-olds, particularly girls, as an indicator of success in this area. However, success in achieving our aim will depend on changing attitudes and behaviour towards smoking across a range of ages from 11 onwards.

Aim: **to halt the rise in children smoking**

Target: **to reduce smoking among children from 13% to 9% or less by the year 2010; with a fall to 11% by the year 2005. This will mean approximately 110,000 fewer children smoking in England by the year 2010.**

Note: This target is for improvements measured against a baseline of 13 per cent smoking prevalence among 11-15 year olds in 1996. Children smoking in this target means those aged 11-15 who smoke at least one cigarette a week.

*'our aim is to
re-establish the
downward trend in
smoking among the
adult population
as a whole'*

9.4 Our aim is to re-establish the downward trend in smoking among the adult population as a whole. We also want to tackle the inequalities in smoking between those most in need and those most advantaged. Smoking prevalence among adults over 16 fell from 39 per cent in 1980 to 29 per cent in 1990 (ONS figures). When the previous health strategy, *Health of the Nation*, set its target in 1992, it was against a background of consistently falling smoking rates since the early 1970s. However, despite a further fall to 26 per cent in 1994, the 1996 figure was back at 28 per cent. This suggests that smoking in the adult population may be rising again, which makes our task the more challenging because we must first re-establish a clear downward trend. Our target also reflects our concern to reduce the wide differences in smoking between the social classes as part of a strategy to cut overall smoking rates in the adult population.

Aim: **to establish a new downward trend in adult smoking rates in all social classes**

Target: **to reduce adult smoking in all social classes so that the overall rate falls from 28% to 24% or less by the year 2010; with a fall to 26% by the year 2005. In terms of today's population, this would mean 1.5 million fewer smokers in England.**

Note: This target is for improvements measured against a baseline of 28 per cent smoking prevalence among men and women aged 16 and over in 1996. Adult smoking means anyone aged 16 or over who smokes at least one cigarette a day. The objective is not only to see smoking in all socio-economic groups reduce to a new average figure of 24% by 2010, but also to reduce the difference in smoking rates between manual and non-manual groups. We therefore want to see a rate of change in manual groups similar to or greater than in non-manual groups.

Smoking during pregnancy

9.5 Smoking during pregnancy is a special issue because the health of the child is at stake both during the pregnancy and from breathing parental smoke during childhood. Smoking during pregnancy also strongly reflects the link between smoking and health inequalities, and children living with parents who smoke are more likely to be smokers themselves. We believe it is important to set a specific target for smoking during pregnancy to focus action both in terms of health education and NHS smoking cessation services.

Aim: **to improve the health of expectant mothers and their families**

Target: **to reduce the percentage of women who smoke during pregnancy from 23% to 15% by the year 2010; with a fall to 18% by the year 2005. This will mean approximately 55,000 fewer women in England who smoke during pregnancy.**

Note: This target is for improvements measured against a base line of 23 per cent of women in England who smoked during pregnancy in 1995.

10 Conclusion

10.1 This White Paper will save lives. It contains arguably the most comprehensive strategy to tackle smoking embarked upon anywhere in the world. It represents a huge leap forward in our efforts to reduce smoking in the UK, and is a critical contribution towards achieving the overall aims of our public health strategy and reducing deaths from cancer and heart disease. Informed by evidence and international experience, it covers the whole range of measures needed to tackle this issue.

10.2 We have put together a balanced package of measures. Legislation is used only where required, to implement the EC Directive on the advertising and sponsorship of tobacco products. Where possible, we have looked for partnerships: with local government on under-age sales, with industry on a proof-of-age system, and with the licensed trade on smoking in public places. Individuals have a great part to play in looking after their own health and that of their families.

10.3 We believe that the balance is right and that it will deliver the results we are determined to achieve. But we will be monitoring the outcomes closely. If it looks as though some of the measures may not be as effective as we hoped, we will be ready to re-examine particular problems and to consider tougher action. While our aim is to make existing legislation work better, we will not rule out the option of new legislation in particular areas if it becomes the only realistic way to make progress, all other avenues having failed to deliver enough.

10.4 Smoking kills in England, Scotland, Wales and Northern Ireland. That is why this White Paper sets out a strategy for the UK as a whole. The new Parliament in Scotland, and Assemblies in Wales and Northern Ireland, will each have an important role to play in implementing this White Paper.

Milestones

2010

1.5 million fewer smokers
Our Healthier Nation cancer and circulatory diseases targets

30 July 2006

All tobacco sponsorship ends

2005

Targets for children, adults and pregnant women

30 July 2003

General tobacco sponsorship ends

April 2000

Funds for smoking cessation available throughout the NHS

Autumn 1999

New media campaign launched

July 1999

Regulations to ban poster/print tobacco advertising

April 1999

Funding for smoking cessation services begins

February-March 1999

Consultations on:
• draft regulations to end tobacco advertising
• Approved Code of Practice for workplace smoking policies

December 1998

White Paper published

10.4 The measures in this document will roll-out over different
timescales. The key dates are above.

'each measure is important for the success of the overall package'

Overall action plan

10.5 This is a list of the measures we are taking. It is difficult to weigh the impact of each measure, but together they form a comprehensive package which the evidence from other countries shows will be effective. Each measure is important for the success of the overall package.

- *End tobacco advertising, promotion and sponsorship.* We will bring forward regulations in 1999 to implement the EC Directive. Before that we will consult with business and industry on our plans.

- *Minimal tobacco advertising in shops.* We have agreed with specialist tobacconists that no advertising which could appeal to children appears on the outside of their shops. For shops in general, the regulations to implement the Directive will be drafted to protect children from exposure to tobacco advertising whilst taking account of the need of retailers to display products and prices for existing smokers.

- *Tobacco tax increases.* The Chancellor has already announced increases in tobacco taxes of, on average at least 5% a year in real terms.

- *Action against tobacco smuggling.* We are embarking on a major new offensive against tobacco smuggling and fraud, part of a £35m project.

- *Pressure for European-wide fiscal action.* We will continue to press our fellow EU members for changes in the EC rules so that we can maximise the effectiveness of our taxation policy.

- *New NHS services to help smokers give up.* We will invest up to £60m over the next three years in specialist advice and support on the NHS for smokers wanting to quit.

- *A week's free NRT on the NHS.* Starter packs of nicotine replacement therapy will be available, free of charge to the worst off, with specialist support to help motivated quitters get on the fast-track to giving up for good.

- *Tackling smoking will be a priority for the NHS as part of a new emphasis on disease prevention.* The importance of helping smokers to quit is stressed in priorities guidance to the NHS and health professionals.

- *Co-operation with the pharmaceutical industry.* We will work with pharmaceutical companies and pharmacists to raise public awareness of the potential benefits of NRT and to give practical help and advice to smokers in pharmacies.

- *Mass media health promotion campaign.* We will invest over £50m over the next three years in an evidence-based campaign to change attitudes and behaviour, signpost local cessation services and give direct support and information. It will focus in particular on children and young people, working class smokers and smoking during pregnancy. Parallel campaigns will be run in Scotland, Wales and Northern Ireland.

- *An Approved Code of Practice on smoking in the workplace.* The Health and Safety Commission will consult on an Approved Code of Practice on smoking in the workplace, to clarify the requirements of existing Health and Safety at Work legislation. Consultation will begin in Spring 1999.

- *Choice for non-smokers and smokers in pubs and restaurants.* Representatives of the licensed trade have agreed to make year-on-year improvements in facilities for non-smokers and smokers. Signs inside and outside licensed premises will enable customers and staff to choose. Progress will be independently monitored and we will agree targets for improvements.

- *Smoking policy reviews in all Government buildings.* All Government Departments will be conducting full reviews of internal smoking policies. Policies will reflect the HSC's new Approved Code of Practice.

- *Tough enforcement of law against sales of tobacco to children.* We will work with local government enforcement representatives to develop guidance on how to implement obligations under the law.

- *A single, cross-industry proof of age card.* We will work to bring together and encourage the manufacturers of all age-restricted products to develop a national scheme.

- *Support for Europe-wide initiatives to protect health.* The European Commission is considering proposals to be put to the Health Council in the first half of 1999. We look forward to seeing the proposals and to working constructively with our fellow Member States.

- *Tough industry code to prevent sales to children from vending machines.* The National Association of Cigarette Machine Operators have strengthened their code governing the siting of cigarette vending machines to prevent their use by under 16s.

- *Non-promotion of tobacco products, or events overseas.* UK embassies and high commissions will be taking care to avoid involvement in events which advertise or promote tobacco products overseas.

- *Full support for international tobacco control work.* We are fully committed to international efforts to tackle smoking under the auspices of the World Health Organisation.

- *Reform of CAP regime to cut tobacco growing in the EU.* Farmers subsidised by the EU to grow tobacco will be offered one-off lump sum payments to give up their "quotas".

SMOKING AND JOINED-UP GOVERNMENT

The whole of Government is engaged in the tackling smoking:

- Co-operation between Departments in England, Scotland, Wales and Northern Ireland to ensure a UK-wide approach

- DTI and DCMS involved in minimising detrimental impact on sport and retail industries of EC Directive to end tobacco advertising

- HM Customs and Excise-led strategy to tackle tobacco smuggling and fraud

- HM Customs and Excise also providing pressure on EU duty limits

- HMT committed to tobacco duty increases

- DH contributing cash for NHS smoking cessation services and mass media awareness campaign, and working with the pharmaceutical industry

- HSC to consult on Approved Code of Practice on work place smoking

- DH has agreed a Charter on smoking in public places with the hospitality industry

- DTI working with the ventilation and air conditioning equipment sector and the Atmosphere Improves Results industry initiative to improve the installation and maintenance of equipment

- All departments signed up to review internal smoking policies

- DH and Home Office working with industry to develop a proof-of-age system

- Home Office to explore a new criminal sanction for repeated conviction for sales of tobacco to under 16s

- Local government committed to tougher enforcement

- European Commission to looking at tar, nicotine, labelling regulations

- DFID working with the WHO to tackle smoking internationally

- MAFF backing the new quota buy-back scheme to reduce EU tobacco growing

- DfEE tackling smoking through the Healthy Schools Initiative

WHO WE HAVE CONSULTED

We consulted, or received representations from, the following:

Action on Smoking and Health (ASH)
Alliance of Independent Retailers
Area Health Promotion Managers (Scotland)
ASH (Scotland)
Asian Business Network
Association for Business Sponsorship of the Arts
Association for Non Smokers' Rights
Association of Community Health Councils for England and Wales
Association of Convenience Stores
Association of Independent Tobacco Specialists
Association of Licensed Multiple Retailers
Brewer Blackler Ltd
Brewers and Licensed Retailers Association
British Darts Organisation
British Dental Association
British Dental Health Foundation
British Diabetic Association
British Greyhound Racing Board
British Heart Foundation
British Horse Racing Board
British Hospitality Association
British Institute of Innkeeping
British Licensed Retailers Association
British Lung Foundation
British Medical Association
British Retail Consortium
British Thoracic Society
Business in Sport and Leisure
Cancer Research Campaign
Central Council of Physical Recreation
Chartered Society of Physiotherapy
Clay Pigeon Shooting Association
Co-operative Retail Society
College of Occupational Therapists
Committee of General Practice Education Directors
Community Practitioner and Health Visitors' Association

Company Chemists Association

Confederation of British Industry

Conference of Post Graduate Medical Deans

Consumer Health Information Centre

Convention of Scottish Local Authorities

Coronary Prevention Group

Council of Heads of Medical Schools and Deans of UK Faculties
of Medicine

Douwe Egberts Coffee System

England & Wales Cricket Board

English National Board for Nursing, Midwifery and Health Visiting

English Pool Association

English Sports Council

Essex County Council Trading Standards

Faculty of General Dental Practitioners

Faculty of Public Health Medicine of the Royal College of Physicians

Fédération International de l'Automobile

Fédération International Motocycliste

Federation of Licensed Victualers Associations

Foundation for the Study of Infant Deaths

Freedom Organisation for the Right to Enjoy Smoking Tobacco

Gallaher Group plc

General Dental Council

General Medical Council

Glyndebourne

Guild of Healthcare Pharmacists

Health Education Authority

Health Education Board for Scotland

Ice Hockey Super League

Imperial Cancer Research Fund

Imported Tobacco Products Advisory Council

Institute of Sports Sponsorship

Joint Hospitality Industry Congress

King's Fund Policy Institute

Lawn Tennis Association

Licensed Victualers Association

Local Authorities Co-ordinating body on Food and Trading Standards

Local Government Association

London Symphony Orchestra

Marie Curie Cancer Care

Multiple Newsagents Association

National Association of Cigarette Machine Operators

National Association of Fund Holding Practices

National Asthma Campaign

National Childbirth Trust

National Federation of Anglers

National Federation of Retail Newsagents

National Federation of Sea Anglers

National Heart Forum

National Opera Studio

National Osteoporosis Society

National Pharmaceutical Association

NHS Alliance

No Smoking Day

North Yorkshire CC Trading Standards

Northern Ireland Centre for Postgraduate Pharmaceutical Education

Novartis

Outdoor Advertising Association

PGA European Tour

Patients' Association

Periodical Publishers Association

Peter Stuyvesant Foundation Ltd

Petrol Retailers Association

Pharmacia and Upjohn

Professional Golfers' Association

Proprietary Association of Great Britain

QUIT

RAC Motorsports Association

Restaurant Association

Retail Confectioners and Tobacconists Association

Roy Castle Lung Cancer Foundation

Royal College of Anaesthetists

Royal College of General Practitioners

Royal College of Midwives

Royal College of Nursing

Royal College of Obstetricians and Gynaecologists

Royal College of Paediatrics and Child Health

Royal College of Physicians

Royal College of Psychiatrists

Royal College of Surgeons of England

Royal Pharmaceutical Society of Great Britain

Royal Society of Health
Royal Yachting Association
Rugby Football League
Scottish Licensed Trade Association
SmithKline Beecham
Society of Occupational Medicine
Stroke Association
Tobacco Control Alliance
Tobacco Manufacturers' Association
Tobacco Workers Alliance
Trades Union Congress
Ulster Orchestra
United Kingdom Central Council for Nursing, Midwifery and Health Visiting
United Kingdom Sports Council
Vendome Luxury Group PLC
Wholesale Confectionery & Tobacco Trade Alliance Ltd
World Development Movement
World Professional Billiards and Snooker Association
World Wide Brands

References

1. Callum C. *The UK smoking epidemic: deaths in 1995.* London: Health Education Authority, 1998.

2. Peto R, Lopez AD, Boreham J, Thun M, Heath Jr C. Mortality from tobacco in developed countries: indirect estimation from national vital statistics. *Lancet* 1992; **339**: 1268-78.

3. *Our Healthier Nation.* Consultation Paper presented to Parliament by the Secretary of State for Health. February 1998. London: The Stationery Office, 1998.

4. Wald N, Nicolaides-Bouman A, eds. *UK Smoking Statistics.* Oxford: Oxford University Press, 1988.

5. The figure of 13 million smokers is based on estimates of cigarette smokers in the UK, obtained from the following sources:
    Thomas M, Walker A, Wilmot A, Bennett N, Office for National Statistics. *Living in Britain: results from the 1996 General Household Survey.* London: The Stationery Office, 1998.
    ONS Monitor Population and Health 1996, PP1 97\1. London: Office for National Statistics, 28 August 1997.
    Northern Ireland Continuous Household Survey, 1996/7. Northern Ireland Statistics and Research Agency, 1997.

6. Thomas M, Walker A, Wilmot A, Bennett N, Office for National Statistics. *Living in Britain: results from the 1996 General Household Survey.* London: The Stationery Office, 1998.

7. *Lifestyle Changes in Wales.* Health in Wales Survey 1996. (Technical Report no 27).

8. *Northern Ireland Continuous Household Survey,* 1996/7. Northern Ireland Statistics and Research Agency, 1997.

9. Lindsey Jarvis, Office for National Statistics. *Smoking among secondary school children in 1996: England.* London: The Stationery Office, 1997

10. Joosens L. *The effectiveness of banning advertising for tobacco products.* International Union Against Cancer, October 1997.

11. World Health Organisation. *Health for all.* Database: European region, 1998

12. Pierce JP, Gilpin EA, Emery SL, White MM, Rosbrook B, Berry CC. Has the California tobacco control program reduced smoking? *JAMA* 1998; **280**: 893-899.

13. Peto R, Lopez AD, Boreham J *et al.*: Imperial Cancer Research Fund and World Health Organisation. *Mortality from smoking in developing countries 1950-2000.* Oxford: Oxford University Press, 1994.

14. Office for National Statistics. *Population Trends Number 93, Autumn 1998.* London: The Stationery Office, 1998.

15. Doll R, Peto R. The causes of cancer: quantitative estimates of avoidable risks of cancer in the United States today. *J Natl Cancer Inst* 1981; **66**: 1191-1308.

16. Law MR, Hackshaw AK. A meta-analysis of cigarette smoking, bone mineral density and risk of hip fracture: recognition of a major effect. *BMJ* 1997; **315**: 841-846.

17. Meltzer M, Gill B, Petticrew M, Hinds K, Office for Population and Census Surveys. *Surveys of Psychiatric Morbidity, Report 3: Economic activty and social functioning of adults with psychiatric disorders.* London: Her Majesty's Stationery Office, 1994.

18. Doll R, Crofton J, eds. *British Medical Bulletin: Tobacco and Health.* London: The Royal Society of Medicine Press, 1996; (vol 52).

19. Buck D, Godfrey C, Parrott S, Raw M, University of York Centre for Health Economics. *Cost effectiveness of smoking cessation interventions.* London: Health Education Authority, 1997.

20. Hackshaw AK, Law M, Wald NJ. The accumulated evidence on lung cancer and environmental tobacco smoke. *BMJ* 1997; **315**: 980-8.

21. Law MR, Morris JK, Wald NJ. Environmental tobacco smoke exposure and ischaemic heart disease: an evaluation of the evidence. *BMJ* 1997; **315**: 973-80.

22. Cook DG, Strachan DP, Anderson Ross H. Series of papers: health effects of passive smoking. *Thorax* 1997-1998. Eds Britton JR, Weiss ST.

23. Royal College of Physicians of London. *Smoking and the young: a report of a working party of the Royal College of Physicians.* London: Royal College of Physicians, 1992.

24. Department of Health and Social Security, Department of Health and Social Services Northern Ireland, Scottish Home and Health Department. *Fourth report of the Independent Scientific Committee on Smoking and Health.* London: Her Majesty's Stationery Office, 1988. Chairman: Sir P Froggatt.

25. Peto R, Jarvis M. [Personal communication.]

26. Drever F, Whitehead M, eds. *Health inequalities: decennial supplement: Office for National Statistics.* London: The Stationery Office, 1997. (Series DS; no. 15).

27. Acheson D. *Independent inquiry into inequalities in health.* London: The Stationery Office, 1998. Chairman: Sir D Acheson.

28. Dorset R, Marsh A. *The Health Trap – Poverty, Smoking and Lone Parenthood.* London (1998). The Policy Studies Institute.

29. Labour Party. *New Labour because Britain deserves better.* London: Labour Party, 1997.

30. Townsend J, Roderick P, Cooper J. Cigarette smoking by socioeconomic group, sex, and age: effects of price, income, and health publicity. *BMJ* 1994; **309**: 923-927.

31. Sutton S. How ordinary people in Great Britain perceive the health risks of smoking. *J Epidemiol Community Health* 1998; **52**: 338-339.

32. Freeth S. *Smoking-related behaviour and attitudes, 1997: a report on research using the ONS Omnibus Survey produced on behalf of the Department of Health.* London: The Stationery Office, 1998.

33. United States Department of Health and Human Services. *The health benefits of smoking cessation - a report of the Surgeon General.* US DHHS. Public Health Service, Centers for Disease Control. Center for Chronic disease prevention and health promotion. Office on smoking and health. DHHS Publication number (CDC) 90-8416,1990.

34. Raw M, McNeill A, West R. Smoking Cessation Guidelines for Health Professionals. A Guide to Effective Smoking Cessation Interventions for the Health Care System. *Thorax*, December 1998, **53**, Supplement 5.

35. Anthonisen NR, Connett JE, Kiley JP, et al. Effects of smoking intervention and the use of an inhaled anticholinergic bronchodilator on the rate of decline of FEV1: the Lung Health Study. *JAMA* 1994; **272**: 1497-1505.

36. QUIT, Helping Smokers to Quit. London: QUIT, 1994, updated 1996.

37. Fowler G. *BMJ* 1997; **314**: 1827 and references cited therein.

38.   Marsh A, McKay S. *Poor smokers.* London: Policy Studies Institute, 1994. (Research Report; no. 771).

39.   Hecht SS, Carmella SG, Chen ML, Salzberger U, Tollner U, Lackmann GM. Metabolites of the tobacco-specific lung carcinogen 4-(methylnitrosoamino)-1-(3-pyridyl)-1-butanone (nnk) in the urine of newborn infants. *Abstracts Papers Am Chem Soc* 1998: **216**; 32.

40.   Foster K, Lader D, Cheesbrough S. *Infant Feeding 1995: Office for National Statistics.* London: The Stationery Office, 1997.

41.   University of York NHS Centre for Reviews and Dissemination, *Effectiveness Matters,* (1998), Vol 3, Issue 1.

42.   Barron J. *Young teenagers and smoking in 1997.* London: Office for National Statistics.

43.   Bjartviet K, Lund KE. *The Norwegian ban on advertising of tobacco products: has it worked?* Norwegian Cancer Society & Norwegian Health Association.

44.   Health Education Authority, London. [Unpublished research.]

45.   Health and Safety Executive. *Passive smoking at work.* Sheffield: Health and Safety Executive, 1998.

46.   Cigarette wars in Africa. *Lancet* 1997; **350**: 793.

47.   Office for National Statistics: Business Monitor 210: Q2. *Overseas trade analysed in terms of Industries.* London: The Stationery Office, 1998.

48.   Parrott S, Godfrey C, Raw M, West R, McNeill A. Guidance for Commissioners on the Cost Effectiveness of Smoking Cessation Interventions. *Thorax* December 1998, **53**, Supplement 5.

This document can be accessed on the Internet at the following address:
www.official-documents.co.uk/document/cm41/4177/4177htm

Printed in the UK for The Stationery Office Limited on behalf of the
Controller of Her Majesty's Stationery Office
Dd 5068514, 12/98, 5673. Job No J 68008